BRAVE NEW NHS?

The impact of the new genetics on the health service

Jo Lenaghan

INSTITUTE FOR PUBLIC POLICY RESEARCH

INSTITUTE FOR PUBLIC POLICY RESEARCH

30-32 Southampton St
London WC2E 7RA
Tel: 0171 470 6100
Fax: 0171 470 6111
ippr@easynet.co.uk
www.ippr.org.uk
Registered charity 800065

The Institute for Public Policy Research is an independent charity whose purpose is to contribute to public understanding of social, economic and political questions through research, discussion and publication. It was established in 1988 by leading figures in the academic, business and trade-union communities to provide an alternative to the free market think tanks.

IPPR's research agenda reflects the challenges facing Britain and Europe. Current programmes cover the areas of economic and industrial policy, Europe, governmental reform, human rights, defence, social policy, the environment and media issues.

Besides its programme of research and publication, IPPR also provides a forum for political and trade union leaders, academic experts and those from business, finance, government and the media, to meet and discuss issues of common concern.

Trustees

Lord Eatwell (Chairman)
Gail Rebuck (Secretary)
Robert Gavron (Treasurer)
Professor Tony Atkinson
Professor Kumar Bhattacharyya
Rodney Bickerstaffe
Lord Brooke
James Cornford

John Edmonds
Professor Anthony Giddens
Lord Hollick
Philip Hughes
Sir Jeremy Isaacs
Professor David Marquand
Jan Royall

Production & design by **EMPHASIS**
ISBN 1 86030 077 4
© IPPR 1998
Printed and bound in Great Britain by Biddles Ltd, Guildford and King's Lynn

Contents

Acknowledgements

Many thanks to Anna Coote, former Deputy Director of IPPR, who initiated and directed this research project, and read and commented on several early papers and drafts. A special acknowledgement must go to Liz Kendall, who carried out the first year of research on this project, before leaving to work as a special advisor to Harriet Harman MP. The excellent work by Liz Kendall provided an invaluable foundation for the final report. Many thanks to Vicki Combe who provided editorial and research assistance in the final preparation of this report.

I would also like to thank the following members of an advisory board who generously gave comments and advice on the five papers which formed the basis for the final report: Rachel Bartlett, Angus Clarke, Dr. Julia Dorin, Dr. Hilary Harris, Jane Franklin, Dr. Robin Fears, Alistair Kent, Rachel Iredale, Beth-Lee Jones, Professor Bernadette Modell, Nick Scott-Ram, Dr. John Sime and Tom Wilke.

Special thanks go the following who read early drafts of this report and patiently corrected my many mistakes and misconceptions: Rachel Bartlett, Angus Clarke, Anna Coote, Dr. Hilary Harris, Alistair Kent, Rachel Iredale, Professor Bernadette Modell and Dr. Ron Zimmern.

Finally, although I am grateful for all the comments and help which I received from the above, the views contained in this report are those of the author alone, and do not necessarily represent the views of those who so kindly gave their advice.

We would especially like to thank SmithKline Beecham who have generously supported IPPR's work on genetics. In particular we would like to acknowledge their patience and tolerance in the face of unexpected delays, and for allowing us total freedom in both the process and content of the final report.

About the author

Jo Lenaghan is a Research Fellow in Health Policy at IPPR. She was formerly a Clinical Audit Co-ordinator in the National Health Service, and a Research Officer for a charity for people suffering from asbestos related illnesses. The main focus of her work so far has been on health care rationing and patients' rights and developing innovative methods for involving the public in decisions about health care policy. She is currently co-ordinating the Policy Forum on the Future of Health and Health Care in the UK, which has been set up to consider the key policy questions facing the NHS in the millenium. Most recently she has edited *Rethinking IT in Healthcare* (1998) for IPPR and *Hard Choices in Health Care* for BMJ Publishing (1997), and is author of *Rationing and Rights in Healthcare* (1996) IPPR, and co-author with Anna Coote of *Citizen's Juries: Theory into practice* (1997), IPPR.

Summary

If the potential of genetics is to be realised, health professionals and policy makers must understand the opportunities and challenges which lie ahead. This report provides an analysis of the current provision of genetic services in the UK, identifies the key issues and questions for the future, proposes specific policies where appropriate and maps out an agenda for further discussion and debate:

- What impact will future developments in the new genetics have on our ability to prevent, diagnose and treat disease?

- Which genetic services should be provided by the NHS and why?

- What issues do developments in genetics raise for purchasers and providers of health care?

- Should genetic tests be supplied direct to the public?

- Who should have access to genetic information?

- How can we ensure that the NHS is in the driving seat of change?

Introduction

By the beginning of the next century, it is anticipated that all fields of medicine will be utilising genetic advances in their practice. Since genes underlie all biological functions, understanding their mode of action will give new insights into the processes disrupted in disease, may open up new avenues for prevention and treatment, and have profound implications for the ways in which we deliver and access health care services in the next century.

Yet these fundamental changes have not been accompanied by a wide or informed debate about the impact of the new genetics on the National Health Service. The issues which the new genetics will raise for the NHS have hardly been identified, let alone debated

This publication aims to fill this policy gap, by identifying the key issues which genetics will raise for those who provide, use and fund the health service over the next decade. Our objective is to take the debate about genetics out of the rather exclusive world of science and ethics, putting it right at the heart of the health service. The combination of ongoing changes in both the science of genetics and the infrastructure which will deliver genetics as a service, will require policy makers alert to the challenges ahead and clear about what it is we are trying to achieve.

Brave New NHS? provides an analysis of how genetic services are currently organised in the UK and highlights the issues and problems which policy makers and health care professionals will need to address. Where appropriate, we propose practical policies, but are conscious that given the pace of anticipated change, we must avoid being too rigid or prescriptive about future strategies. Some chapters are therefore more speculative in approach, and highlight issues for future debate. Some of the issues and recommendations are summarised here.

Genetic futures

Many clinicians and commentators disagree about the likely pace and nature of developments in genetic science in the future, and the uses to which the emerging knowledge can and should be put. The 'enthusiasts' believe that advances in knowledge about the human genome will not only affect the rare, single gene disorders such as cystic fibrosis, sickle cell disease and Huntington's disease, but provide new opportunities for the treatment and management of the common diseases, including diabetes, cancer, cardiovascular disease, arthritis, some mental disorders, asthma and Alzheimer's disease.

Other more cautious commentators point out that the precise contribution of the relevant genes in such diseases is not yet understood, and that our ability to identify a gene may not necessarily translate into opportunties for prevention or effective treatment. It is impossible to predict which future will prevail. It is likely that developments will occur at different rates for different diseases with different clinical implications. Increased understanding of the genetic components of disease may lead to:

● *A new way of classifying disease*
Diseases are currently classified according to their symptoms, the disease phenotype. Describing a condition purely according to its appearance could obscure the underlying causes of many common diseases. Increasing knowledge about the genotype (the genetic

make-up of a cell or individual) may lead to a better understanding of the biochemical or physiological causes of disease.

● *The possibility of earlier detection and prevention*
The NHS is currently based upon a model which aims to 'diagnose and treat' a condition. In the future, genetics may increasingly move the practice of medicine towards a 'predict and prevent' model. Genetic testing may offer the potential to identify at-risk individuals, with opportunities for preventative measures such as education about life-style changes, and monitoring for early diagnosis and treatment.

● *The ability to provide better targeted and more effective treatment*
Since many treatments have tended to concentrate on relieving the symptoms, rather than the causes of disease, a better understanding of disease mechanisms could enable a more rational approach to the development of treatments and therapies. Drugs may increasingly be designed to fit the specific molecular processes involved in causing disease, and be targeted at those most likely to benefit.

NHS professionals and policy makers must understand the uncertainty that surrounds the future role of genes in disease diagnosis, cure and prevention and the need to maintain a flexible and critical approach to the future as it unfolds.

Which genetic services should be provided and why?

New techniques in genetics have made it possible to identify and isolate specific genes involved in important human disorders. As the technology develops, questions for the NHS include *how*, *when* and *why* which kind of genetic tests or screening programmes should actually be introduced into the health service, who should make these decisions, and according to what criteria.

Criteria for genetic testing and screening

In order to enable the NHS to develop a coherent strategy for the introduction of genetic tests and screening programmes, several questions need to be addressed. What level and kind of accuracy should the NHS require before agreeing to fund genetic tests and screening programmes? Is it appropriate to provide a test for a disease if there is no cure? How should the NHS respond to public demand for tests of limited benefit? Should tests be provided on a population basis or targeted at those already considered at high risk? Will genetic screening programes result in more harm than benefit? What is the overall aim of genetic services? These are complex issues, which are discussed in detail in the report. We argue that exisiting mechanisms or paradigms for making these decisions in the health service are not appropriate for assessing the new genetics. Criteria developed for testing and screening progammes which are used to identify the early stages of a disease may not be appropriate for a technique which may indicate the probability of a healthy person becoming ill sometime in the future. These issues will be of increasing importance to the NHS, particularly in the light of the Government's proposal to set up a National Institute for Clinical Excellence, to develop and diseminate clinical guidelines on clinical and cost effectiveness.

Review of current decision-making mechanisms

There is currently a lack of a co-ordinated or coherent approach to the development of genetic services in the NHS, and an absence of data on the impact of current service provision. This important gap in our knowledge will act as an impediment to the future development of genetic services. There is an urgent need to:

- *Monitor* current provision of genetic services (testing and screening)

- *Evaluate* different models of provision

- *Disseminate* best practice and guidelines

The Conservative Government reacted to calls for a national co-ordinated strategy to deal with issues raised by genetics in an *ad hoc* and incoherent way. In the space of less than a year, they created the National Screening Committee, the Advisory Committee on Genetic Testing and the Human Genetics Advisory Commission. Including the Gene Therapy Advisory Group, we now have four bodies looking at different aspects of genetic developments. This results in a lack of co-ordination and coherence, with responsibilities either missed or repeated by the various committees.

Both the Advisory Committee on Genetic Testing (ACGT) and the National Screening Committee (NSC) have made an impressive contribution towards resolving dilemmas raised by the new genetics, and their roles are continuing to evolve. However, the remit and expertise of the NSC does not include genetics. The ACGT has expertise in genetics, but does not look at screening issues.

The last thing we need is yet another new committee or commission. Instead, we recommend that the Department of Health initiates a short but multi-disciplinary review to consider how to weave together the work of existing committees, in order to ensure greater coherence and co-ordination in the future. In particular, the review should consider:

- How to ensure greater vertical and horizontal communication between all the committees and stakeholders

- Who should be responsible for monitoring and evaluating *all* genetic services

- How to ensure the effective dissemination and sharing of best practice

- How the committees might relate and contribute to the emerging work of the National Institute for Clinical Excellence (NICE)

Issues for purchasers

In order to consider how purchasers might appropriately buy genetic services, a number of key questions must first be addressed. How should genetics be measured as a service? How should we define a successful outcome? Who should be involved in these decisions? At what level should genetic services be purchased? Central to all of these issues is the key question which will confront purchasers: what is the aim of genetic services?

What should be the aim of genetic services?

Developments in genetics will enable us to predict the likelihood of future diseases in healthy people, sometimes (though not always) offering opportunities for disease prevention. This will require a paradigm shift in the way in which we think about and measure our health care services in the future.

It is possible to distinguish at least three different purposes or aims for genetic services: *human rights*, (where the key objective is to enable individuals to make better informed decisions about their own health), *utilitarian* (where the aim would be to reduce the prevalence of the disease in the community or population as a whole), and *clinical*, (where a test or screening programme would only be carried out if there is something 'clinically valid' which can be done with the information). The future shape and level of genetic services in the new NHS will be determined by which of these aims the health service signs up to. We therefore recommend:

- An explicit and inclusive debate is needed about the aims of genetic services. The Human Genetics Advisory Commission should facilitate an informed public and professional debate on these issues

- Until the above happens, a reduction in morbidity and mortality should not be used to measure genetic services, although they may sometimes be a consequence of informed choice

- Greater emphasis on positively welcoming children and adults affected by genetic conditions into our society should be encouraged, in order to facilitate informed choices

- Purchasers should have an obligation to be open about their decision-making processes

- We need mechanisms for ensuring that geneticists and public health specialists have the opportunity to share their relevant knowledge and experience at both a local and national level and to contribute to the emerging work of the National Institute for Clinical Excellence.

Ensuring that genetic services are purchased at the appropriate level

The abolition of the internal market and the recognition of the importance of co-operation and collaboration are welcome developments. The new Labour Government is clearly committed to ending division and fragmentation, and ensuring greater equity of access to quality services for all. However, in order to ensure that this aim is achieved in practice, we recommend:

- Genetics should be purchased as a specialist service and commissioned accordingly *at this stage*

- Purchasing arrangements for genetic services should be monitored and kept under review as the new genetics develops

- Future changes in the pattern of health service purchasing must allow for the family based nature of clinical genetics, for the frequent crossing of geographical boundaries and for the need to incorporate new developments.

Issues for providers

During the next decade we are likely to witness important developments in the science of genetics. What was once a service for rare single gene disorders may become increasingly relevant to other common diseases. These anticipated developments will challenge traditional boundaries and divisions between professionals and institutions, and increase the pressure for new structures for delivering genetic services.

Changing Role of Regional Genetic Centres

There appears to be a general consensus that the current model of genetic services based at the regional level has developed around the rare and single gene disorders. As genetics continues to impact on multifactorial and common diseases, this model will no longer be sufficient. Future changes, however, should continue to recognise and facilitate the family based nature of genetic services, and the importance of expertise which is maintained at regional level:

- Consultant Clinical Geneticists (CCGs) based at Regional Genetics Centres will probably continue to provide services for the rare and single gene disorders

- CCGs are expected to play a more active role in the education of other NHS professionals and may form part of Community Genetic Teams.

The increasing importance of primary care

It is generally anticipated that as genetics impacts on the more common diseases, the scope for primary care involvement will increase. There are two possible models for primary care involvement in the provision of genetic services: The GP as *gatekeeper* and guide to genetic services and the GP as *provider* of some genetic services. It is likely that different approaches will be appropriate for different types of disease, and may even depend on the willingness and ability of individual Primary Care Groups. Regardless of which model develops in primary care, the following issues will need to be addressed in order to ensure a high quality service in the future:

- The lack of knowledge and understanding of genetics in primary care must be recognised and addressed. It may be necessary to improve the current standard of genetic services at primary care level before expanding the role of GPs

- GPs must be appropriately trained in understanding genetic knowledge and communicating it to others (counselling techniques)

- The issue of time needs serious consideration, perhaps through a system of guaranteeing minimum consultation times and/or the use of other primary care workers

- Information technology could be used to support decisions and disseminate protocols to ensure appropriate referral patterns

- GPs will need to be encouraged to work collaboratively with other co-workers; the Health Improvement Programmes may support this

- Primary Care Groups may develop different models of care for different diseases, but they should be evaluated so that we can learn from what works

- It is vital that GPs are consulted before developing unrealistic models for the future. Are they willing and able to deliver what is increasingly expected of them?

The role of other NHS professionals and services

If, as expected, genetics becomes a feature of all clinical specialities, developments will have impacts on all aspects of the health service and those who work in it. GPs will not be able to deliver genetic services by themselves and will require a range of co-workers to enable them to meet the needs of their patients. We therefore suggest:

- Genetic Nurse Specialists or co-workers could provide a focus for future developments, linking the Regional Genetic Centres with the community

- Genetic Nurse Specialists (GNS) will need education and training programmes, with a proper career structure in order to ensure that the appropriate staff are attracted and retained

- Community Genetic Teams may provide a useful model for drawing together a range of expertise at the community level

- We should consider how to ensure that (approximately) one in ten of those working in other clinical specialities have a good understanding of genetics, and how they can act as a resource for others

- We should consider ways in which genetics can build on existing patterns of provision where appropriate, such as Family Cancer Clinics

- Future staffing levels and roles need to be driven by competence models, not professional entrenchment.

Genetic tests supplied direct to the public

In the UK, genetic services are currently provided almost exclusively by the NHS. The General Practitioner essentially acts as gatekeeper, and can refer patients to see a Consultant Clinical Geneticist if necessary. Yet what if this gateway to genetic services is kept shut, and the NHS is unable or unwilling to meet predicted demand? Resources are already stretched, and GPs have varying degrees of knowledge or interest in the new genetics. Could or should there be a role for the private sector in providing genetic tests in the future?

Although there is currently a tiny market in the commercial provision of genetic tests, developments in the USA point to the need to anticipate worst case scenarios. Potential public demand for commercial genetic tests must be viewed in the context of a wider cultural shift towards more self medication and patient autonomy. The issue of whether genetic tests differ from other medical tests thereby warranting particular regulation is not clear cut – the answer is likely to be different for different tests and diseases. We suggest that predictive genetic tests are different, but welcome further debate. There are concerns that a commercial market in genetic tests could:

- Inflate inappropriate demand

- Fuel public and patient anxiety

- Leave the NHS to pick up the pieces, in terms of counselling

- Cream off the cheap services

- Erode the principle of equity

- Fail to respect confidentiality

- The conflict between commercial and public interest may result in a dilution of quality

In response to these concerns, the Advisory Committee on Genetic Tests (ACGT) published a Code of Practice for genetic testing offered commercially to the public. The ACGT is not a statutory body, and the Code of Practice offers guidance only. If the market for commercial provision of genetic tests grows, then we recommend the following options should be explored, in an attempt to build upon the excellent work of the ACGT and other bodies:

Development of the ACGT and Code of Practice

- A review of adherence to the Code of Practice should be carried out to identify what (if anything) needs to be made statutory and why

- We anticipate that the ACGT could evolve into a statutory body

- If so, Government should explore other examples of flexible

regulation, as typified by the Human Fertilisation and
Embryology Authority and Health and Safety Commission.

What regulatory functions might the ACGT carry out?

● Develop a pre-market approval system for the public and private
sector (although the ACGT could develop guidelines which
would be enforced by the MCA)

● To avoid restricting progress, any pre-market approval system
should allow for flexibility, possibly through the use of 'stringent
scrutiny'

● Ensure that the NHS only purchases from accredited providers

● Broaden the concept of accreditation to include the concerns of
users.

It is vital that a commercial sector does not develop in response to
the failure of the NHS to meet appropriate demand. Such a
development would result in inequity of access, and create a two-tier
health care system. It is the aim of this publication to ensure that NHS
professionals are prepared for the challenges ahead, so that all citizens
can have access to genetic services on the basis of need and need
alone.

Genetic information, privacy, access and discrimination

The National Health Service does not exist in a social vacuum. The
extent to which the public accept, demand or avoid genetic testing or
screening services in the future will depend in part upon who will have
access to genetic information and how they will use it. A key concern is
not just that these issues will affect future levels of demand, but that
insurance or employer-related use of genetic tests could undermine the
concept of unpressured consent, which is the cornerstone of genetic
testing.

It is therefore essential that those concerned with the future
development of genetic services in the NHS begin to engage with the
debate currently taking place in wider public policy circles: Who should
have access to the results of genetic tests and under what (if any)

conditions? What would be the consequences of (non) access? How can public policy balance the competing claims of privacy and access?

Insurance companies and genetic information

The question of whether insurance companies should have access to genetic test results is likely to influence public perception of and demand for genetic services in the future. Industry fears that without access to genetic test results they will suffer from adverse selection. Health professionals and user groups have expressed fears that if industry does have access, then the public could suffer from genetic discrimination, resulting in a low uptake of tests of potential benefit. However, little evidence exists to support either side. Too little attention has been paid to the distinction between different types of tests and diseases. Rather than lump all genetic tests together, we suggest that it is helpful to ask which (if any) genetic tests are actuarially relevant and which (if any) types of genetic tests will lead to unfair discrimination if insurance companies here access to them, and adverse selection if they don't. Following this analysis, we recommended that:

- Government impose a general moratorium on genetic test results, but consider an exception for a small number of certain genetic tests (such as dominantly inherited single gene disorders of late-on-set)

- An independent monitoring body (as recommended by the HGAC and the citizens' jury) should ensure that the moratorium is respected and monitor how the test results covered by the exemption are treated and with what effect

- The above would provide invaluable evidence to inform the work of the evaluation mechanism recommended by the HGAC to consider actuarial evidence presented in support of specific genetic tests or insurance products.

Employers and genetic information

Too little attention has been given to the potential for discrimination if employers are allowed access to genetic information. There is currently no legislation in place to prevent possible abuse. We therefore recommend:

- The issue of genetic information and employers needs to be put much higher on the public policy agenda

- The current lack of any legal safeguards against abuse is a cause for concern

- Means for preventing or managing employer access to genetic information should be explored, such as privacy laws

- Trade unions and employer organisations should be included in these vital debates

Future issues

Many of the dilemmas discussed above represent our reaction to and understanding of the genetic tests which are currently available. However, the new genetics is a fast moving area of knowledge. Developments in the availability and application of predictive genetic tests, combined with changes in the role of the welfare state will raise important questions about the nature of our society and the responsibilities which individual citizens have for themselves and each other. IPPR will continue to explore the issue of rights and responsibilities in health care, but meanwhile, we raise the following issues:

- We need a public debate to decide which risks should be a matter for individual responsibility and which should be shared

- Policy makers must develop mechanisms that allow risk to be shared where appropriate, such as social insurance systems for long term care

- Policy makers and politicians must strive to develop and encourage policies that emphasise what unites us, and not leave the market to use genetics to divide us.

For the future

This report represents the beginning, rather than the end, of an important debate. In the final chapter, we identify issues which are beyond the capacity of this report, but which merit further debate and research in the years to come.

The cost of genetic services

The problem for policy makers is that there are very few good studies of the cost of the new genetic technologies. There is an urgent need to develop proper analyses of the full cost of genetic services, taking into account the potential impact of patents, public demand and counselling. Such information is essential in order to allow the NHS to plan for the future. Any such analyses must include the views of the user, and a more holistic approach to assessing the costs and benefits of health care in general.

Public demand

The level of public demand for genetic tests and screening programmes will play a crucial role in the future development and costs of genetic services, and may depend upon a complex combination of factors, including public knowledge and perception of genetics in general and of each disease and test in particular. For policy makers, the question is, do we attempt to reduce 'inappropriate demand', or do we try to understand and respond to lay perceptions of risk, and develop services accordingly? If we embark upon a programme of public education, what message should be communicated, by whom, and to what end?

Public education

A general public education programme is desirable, but it is not an acceptable substitute for a high quality and comprehensive genetic counselling service. The public needs a greater understanding of genetics not just in order to help them make choices within their own individual lives and families, but to enable them to participate in debates about the wider use of genetics in society generally. Recent innovative methods have included school based education programmes, theatre productions, citizens' juries, public meetings and referenda. There is a need for an independent evaluation of all of these methods, to assess just how effective each approach is in provoking an informed and wide public debate and understanding.

Public perceptions of and reactions to risk may not necessarily be 'wrong' but merely different to those of professionals. It is important that policy makers understand the ways in which the public may react to the potential choices offered by the new genetics, as this could have profound implications for the uptake and development of genetic services as a whole. The choices people make as a result of genetic tests or screening programmes should be reported and analysed, in order to help the future development of genetic services.

The media, science and public policy

It is increasingly futile to talk about the need for public education or public perceptions of risk without considering one of the most important influences of the late twentieth century: the media. Modern life is an increasingly socially mediated experience, one in which systems of mass communications, both printed and electronic, play a key role. As such, the media has the power not only to inform the public of the challenges and opportunities presented by genetic knowledge, but also shape people's perceptions of developments, either by coverage or omission. The media can play both a mystificatory and de-mystificatory role in relation to modern medicine. Future research needs to consider how to encourage the latter.

The need for a coherent strategy and inclusive debate

The National Health Service must be able to anticipate developments and work flexibly and responsively in order to take advantage of the opportunities offered by the new genetics. Without a strategy, genetic services could be developed in an *ad hoc* manner, subject to the demands of patients, fuelled by industrial and media interests, dependent upon the attitudes and knowledge of individual doctors and obstructed by cash strapped and short sighted health authorities. The aim of this report is to identify the challenges and opportunities ahead and to outline a strategy for managing this period of unpredictable change. Only time will reveal which prediction of the future role of genetics in disease is the most accurate, but the lack of a clear consensus indicates the need for policy makers to avoid being dazzled by the promise of a future that may never materialise, or left behind by changes that they failed to anticipate.

The greater the degree of uncertainty about the future, the greater the need for an open and explicit debate about the principles and aims of the NHS in general and genetic services in particular. The debate on the future development on genetics must be as inclusive as possible, so that we can all participate in shaping the Brave New NHS.

Introduction

By the beginning of the next century, it is anticipated that all fields of medicine will be utilising genetic advances in their practice, as well as in research. Since genes underlie all biological functions, understanding their mode of action will give new insights into the processes disrupted in disease, and may open up new avenues for prevention and treatment. This fundamental change has been compared by some to the microbiological revolution started by Pasteur and Koch in the last century. (Department of Health, 1995)

Yet these fundamental changes have not been accompanied by a wide or informed debate about the impact of the new genetics on the National Health Service. The media is full of stories about genetics, but attention has tended to focus on either individual 'breakthroughs' (such as the discovery of a new gene) or on the ethical dilemmas raised for society (such as our ability to clone sheep). Both of these issues are important and clearly of interest to the public, but what impact will developments in genetics have on the health service? The issues which the new genetics will raise for the NHS have hardly been identified, let alone debated. Yet if the potential of genetics is to be realised, health professionals, the public and policy makers must begin to understand and debate the opportunities and challenges which lie ahead.

How will a health service based upon a model of 'diagnose and cure' react to a technology which provides opportunities for pre-symptomatic prediction and prevention of future disease? How will health care professionals and the public respond to the new language of uncertainty and probability offered by developments in genetics? What will be the level of demand for genetic tests, what will people do with genetic knowledge and with what effect? How can the NHS ensure the appropriate introduction of genetic tests and screening programmes? Who will deliver these services? Will the new genetics reduce or increase health care costs? As Professor David Hunter has recently noted:

> The time is ripe for a thorough appraisal of the policy implications of genetic medicine for the NHS and health policy generally ...The technology may be 10 years or so away, but it is critical that practitioners, managers and policy

makers and the public should have some knowledge and understanding of what lies in store (Hunter, 1998).

This publication aims to fill this policy gap, by identifying the key issues which genetics will raise for those who provide, use and fund the health service over the next decade. Our objective is to take the debate about genetics out of the rather exclusive world of science and ethics, putting it right at the heart of the health service.

In the following chapters we connect up advances in genetic technology with current organisational and cultural changes occuring both within and without the National Health Service, drawing attention to how each of these changes is affecting and affected by the other, in a complex and dynamic relationship. For example, health care services are currently undergoing a period of organisational transition. The recent publication of the Labour Government's White Paper maps out a 'third way' for the future delivery of health care, which puts a greater emphasis on the role of GPs and other primary care practitioners, who will be expected to both purchase and deliver services in the new NHS. (Department of Health, 1997).

At the same time, developments in our understanding of the molecular basis of ill health are challenging traditional boundaries and divisions between professionals and institutions. Genetics, once a service for rare single gene disorders, such as Huntington's disease, is widely anticipated to become relevant to other more common diseases, such as cancer, asthma and Alzheimer's disease. These developments will require a greater role for the GP, yet there is little or no evidence of policy makers considering whether the proposed Primary Care Groups are willing or able to deliver genetic services. The role of primary care is considered in detail in Chapter 4 but the links between organisational, cultural and technological change is a constant theme running throughout this publication.

Brave New NHS? provides an analysis of how genetic services are currently organised in the UK and highlights the issues and problems which policy makers will need to address. Where appropriate, we propose practical policies, but are conscious that, given the pace of anticipated change, we must avoid being too rigid or prescriptive about future strategies. Some Chapters are therefore more speculative in approach, and highlight issues for future debate.

In the first Chapter, we set out to demystify the language of genetics and provide a simple description of the relationship between genes and disease. If the potential of genetics is to be realised, then health professionals and policy makers must understand what this developing technology can and cannot do. We also draw attention to the uncertainty, and indeed controversy, which surrounds competing claims about the likely pace and nature of future developments in genetic technologies, highlighting the need for policy makers to remain flexible in the face of unpredictable change.

Chapter 2 moves on from what is technically feasible, and asks how, when and why which kind of genetic tests or screening programmes should be introduced into the health service, who should make these decisions and according to what criteria. We argue that exisiting mechanisms or paradigms for making these decisions in the health service are not appropriate for assessing the new genetics. Criteria developed for testing and screening progammes which are used to identify the early stages of a disease may not be appropriate for a technique which may indicate the probability of a healthy person becoming ill sometime in the future. These issues will be of increasing importance to the NHS, particularly in the light of the Government's proposal to set up a National Institute for Clinical Excellence (NICE), to develop and diseminate clinical guidelines on clinical and cost effectiveness. (Department of Health, 1997).

These themes are explored further in Chapter 3, where we consider the issues which developments in genetics will raise for purchasers. How will purchasers measure genetics as a service? At what level should genetics be purchased and who should be involved in these decisions? The recent White Paper devolves purchasing responsibility to Primary Care Groups, but will such groups have a sufficient population or knowledge base to puchase services for rare genetic disorders?

The key question which will confront purchasers, at whatever level is: what is the aim of genetics as a service? For example, the traditional focus on clinical outcomes (such as the reduction of the incidence of a disease) may be an inappropriate objective for genetic screening services. The answer to these questions could determine not just the shape of genetic services in the NHS, but the composition of society itself.

What kind of genetic services should be provided by whom and at what level? How many staff will be needed and with what skills? How can we facilitate a co-ordinated and integrated approach to service deilvery? As genetics becomes increasingly relevant to more common diseases, the role of Regional Genetic Centres is expected to change, with major implications for the emerging Primary Care Groups. There are concerns that GPs do not have the time, skills or knowledge to deliver a high quality genetics service. The role of GPs and other NHS professionals in delivering genetic services are considered in detail in Chapter 4.

The NHS does not operate in a vacuum. The provision of and demand for genetic services is likely to be affected by developments outside of the health service. The final three chapters therefore look in detail at other potential drivers of change in genetics, and their likely impact on the NHS. The potential role of commerical providers of genetic servcies is the subject of Chapter 5. Should government encourage or allow the commercial sector to meet the demand for genetic services, or is there a need to regulate or prevent non-NHS activity in this sector? What impact would a private market in genetic services have on the NHS? In this chapter we consider whether genetic tests are different from other types of medical tests, and critically assess current mechanisms for managing the commerical market.

In Chapter 6, we consider issues of privacy, access and discrimination, paying particular attention to insurance and employment. The question of who has access to genetic information, and how they use it, will have a profound effect on how the public perceive and use genetic services. Public demand for genetic services is likely to be one of the key factors in the future development of both public and private genetic services, so it is vital that those concerned with health policy understand and are engaged in these important debates. We also suggest that genetic testing could have major implications for long term care if we continue to move towards a commerical insurance system for this form of care.

In the final Chapter, we identify issues which are beyond the capacity of this report, but which merit further debate and research in the years to come. We consider the potential costs of the new genetics, and the factors that are likely to influence the final bill, such as the patenting of genes. We briefly assess the role of public demand, and the related issue of public education. Finally, we consider the increasingly complex relationship between the media, science, uncertainty and public policy. We conclude by repeating the need for a coherent set of principles to guide the NHS in the future, and highlight the need for policy makers to plan for uncertainty.

With a topic as fast moving and unpredictable as genetics and health care, writing a policy document is fraught with difficulties. As Coote and Hunter have observed: 'Predictions are hazardous, but it is important to consider what Government can do to ensure that the public interest is well served in any event'. (Coote and Hunter, 1996)

The combination of changes in both the science of genetics and the infrastructure which will deliver genetics as a service, will require policy makers alert to the challenges ahead and clear about what it is we are trying to achieve. Many of the changes outlined in the White Paper are not due to take effect until 1999, and the Government is clearly committed to learning from what works and discarding what does not. We therefore have a unique opportunity to consider the impact of recent and future reforms on the provision of genetic services, and to develop a framework for the effective and equitable provision of genetic services in the next century. Professor David Hunter has warned:

> The all too familiar danger is that rapid advances in the discovery of new genetic treatments and the means of applying them will run ahead of the NHS's or society's understanding of them and of their value and limitations. A measured consideration of their implications for public health and society more generally is long overdue ... the subject has hardly been considered by those who advise on, or formulate, national health policy. (Hunter, 1998)

Brave New NHS? represents the beginning of this vital debate. To this end, this report provides an analysis of where we are now, identifies the key issues and questions for the future, proposes specific policies where appropriate and maps out an agenda for further discussion and debate.

1. Genetic futures

The language of genetics can be daunting, confusing and exclusive. Our aim in this first Chapter is to demystify the new genetics and to identify the key issues which these developments will raise for the health service. If the potential of genetics is to be realised, health professionals and policy makers must understand the opportunities and challenges which lie ahead.

Below we describe the relationship between genes and disease, and consider the anticipated nature and pace of developments. We assess the likely impact of the new genetics on the ways in which we detect, classify and treat diseases, identifying the key issues which these developments may raise for the health service. Using a number of clinical case studies, we illustrate the need for a coherent and consistent strategy to enable the NHS to take advantage of the opportunities ahead. Just how this can be achieved is the subject of subsequent Chapters.

By way of introduction, we set out below a summary for the lay reader of the different ways in which genes can cause or make people susceptible to disease.

Genes and disease

The inheritance of all our characteristics, including susceptibility to genetic diseases, is dependent on genes and chromosomes. Genes are the coded instructions that control the growth and development of the body, and are made up a substance called DNA. An alteration (mutation) at even a single position of the DNA sequence may cause serious malfunction of the resulting protein. Modern advances in genetics are due to the ability to study DNA directly (Nuffield Council on Bioethics, 1993). It is estimated that about 75,000 different human genes exist, and they come in matching pairs, one from each parent. Chromosomes are physical structures that carry the genes, rather like beads on a length of string, and are important for ensuring the correct transmission of genes through cell division (Clarke, 1997e.)

Genetic disorders

Genetic disorders can be classified into the following categories: single gene disorders, multifactorial or polygenic disorders and chromosomal disorders. It is important to understand the distinction between each type, as different policy questions may be raised by different types of disorders.

Single gene disorders

This is an umbrella term for conditions which are usually inherited (although some conditions can have a high rate of spontaneous mutation). Examples include:

- Muscular dystrophy

- Cystic fibrosis

- Sickle cell anaemia

- Thalassaemia

- Huntington's disease

These diseases arise from fundamental defects in a single gene that we cannot yet cure. In single gene disorders, (also known as Mendelian), there is a strong causal link. If the particular genetic mutation is found then the outcome will be almost certain. For example, a person who tests positive for Huntington's disease is 99 per cent certain to develop this fatal condition. Single gene disorders are usually rare, although some, like sickle cell disease, can be more common in specific sectors of the population. Dominant inheritance is where a single faulty (mutated) gene inherited from one parent is involved (Huntington's disease is an example of this type), whereas in recessive disorders, the condition does not develop unless both copies of the gene that are inherited are faulty (for example, cystic fibrosis).

Multifactorial/polygenic disorders

These diseases have a more complex aetiology, involving the interaction of several environmental and genetic factors. Many common adult disorders are thought to have a considerable genetic component, causing an increased susceptibility to disease, and include:

- Some cancers

- Coronary artery disease

- Diabetes

In multifactorial diseases, the significance of genetic factors, and the extent to which there may be an interaction with the environment, is as yet unclear. Unlike single gene disorders, the role of genes is not directly causal, and we talk instead of 'genetic susceptibility'. As the Nuffield Council on Bioethics has explained:

> Several different genes appear to influence susceptibility, but how they interact with each other, and the relative importance of genetic inheritance and environmental factors as causes of these diseases are still largely unknown (Nuffield Council on Bioethics, 1993).

It is generally anticipated that in the near future the emphasis will shift from rare single gene disorders, towards the common multifactorial conditions.

Chromosomal disorders

Chromosomal disorders are not normally inherited, and can be the result of a spontaneous mutation. There are two types of chromosomal disorders: those where an entire chromosome is added or missing, as in Down's syndrome (where there is an extra copy of chromosome 21) or in Turner's syndrome, where one of the X chromosomes in girls is missing. This type of disorder is not inherited but occurs during conception. In the second type, which can be inherited, a rearrangement of chromosomal material can occur, which can result in harmful clinical effects (Nuffield Council on Bioethics, 1993).

It is important to remember that Mendelian diseases can be subsumed in multifactorial diseases, (for example, the *BRCA1/2* gene accounts for five per cent of all breast cancers) so the distinction used above, whilst helpful, is not as black and white as it looks.

Box 1.1

Single gene disorders	Multifactorial disorders
characterised by	*characterised by*
Strong causal link between gene and disease	Complex interaction between genes and environment
Outcome predetermined	Susceptibility to disease
Rare	Common
Presympomatic tests	Predispostional tests
Formed basis of current practice	Future of genetic services?
examples include	*examples include*
Cystic fibrosis	Some cancers
Sickle cell	Coronary artery disease
Huntington's disease	Diabetes
Muscular dystrophy	Alzheimer's disease

Pace and nature of developments

What impact will our increasing knowledge about the relationship between genes and disease have on the health service? Unfortunately, the answer to this question is not clear cut, and indeed, is subject to controversy. Many clinicians and commentators disagree about the likely pace and nature of developments in genetic science in the future, and the uses to which the emerging knowledge can and should be put. It is imperative that policy makers and NHS professionals are aware of the uncertainty that surrounds the future role of genes in disease diagnosis, cure and prevention, and maintain a flexible and critical approach to the future as it unfolds.

Enthusiasts and cautionists

Speaking at the Royal College of Physicians Lumleian Lecture in May 1997, Sir Richard Sykes, Chairman and Chief Executive of Glaxo Wellcome plc outlined the significance of recent and future genetic developments, concluding that:

> The dramatic rate of progress in genomic research means
> that many genes associated with the common diseases will
> be identified within the next two to three years ...The
> revolution is much closer than you might think (Skyes,
> 1997).

But to what extent will genetics bring about a 'revolution' in health
care and when? Richard Sykes was expressing what might be called the
'enthusiastic' view. Proponents of this view argue that as our
understanding of genetics begins to be translated into possibilities for
prevention and therapy, the emphasis will shift from rare genetic
disorders, towards common conditions central to all medical
specialities. They believe that advances in knowledge about the human
genome will not only affect the rare, single gene disorders such as cystic
fibrosis, sickle cell and Huntington's disease, but provide new
opportunities for the treatment and management of the common
diseases, including diabetes, cancer, cardiovascular disease, arthritis,
some mental disorders, asthma and Alzheimer's disease.

This view is not restricted to representatives of industry, who may
have a vested interest in talking up the potential offered by genetic
developments. The Department of Health (DoH) has predicted that
many of the most important human disease genes are likely to be
identified within the next five years (Department of Health, 1995).
John Bell, Nuffield Professor of Clinical Medicine has also written
that:

> ... it would be surprising if most of the major genetic factors
> involved in human disease were not identified over the next
> five to ten years. This information will form an important
> template for redefining disease, clarifying biological
> mechanisms responsible for disease and developing new
> treatment for most disorders (Bell, 1998).

Bell argues that the use of genetic information in clinical practice has
previously been limited by our technological abilities. The advent of
oligonucleotide array technology or 'chips' will, he claims, solve many
of these problems and allow us to take full advantage of genetic
knowledge.

However, other more cautious commentators are quick to point out that although increasing genetic knowledge may facilitate a better understanding of disease mechanisms, it is by no means certain that this will lead to clear and certain diagnoses and treatments. Holtzman and Shapiro argued in the *British Medical Journal* that the genetics of many diseases are extremely complicated and that tests have only a limited ability to predict the clinical outcome accurately. Variable expressivity, incomplete penetrance, and genetic heterogeneity all reduce the ability of genetic tests to predict future disease accurately, even when single genes have a prominent role. The authors claim that in the vast majority of diseases, multiple genes are likely to be implicated, and unless a test can identify all of the possible combinations, it will have low predictive value. They also point to the fact that relatively few interventions have yet been devised to improve the outcome of most Mendelian disorders, and argue:

> Despite these limitations, exaggerated claims are made for genetic testing and providers and the public are given incomplete and sometimes misleading information about tests (Holtzman & Shapiro, 1998).

For example, although the single gene which causes Huntington's disease was identified in 1993, we still have little understanding of the role that the gene plays, and have no effective therapy or cure for this fatal disease. Whilst accepting that the genetic components of many common disorders are now being identified, critics point out that the precise contribution of the relevant genes is not yet understood (Department of Health, 1995). Others have warned that:

> Physicians need to recognise the limitations of the new information and the commercial pressures behind the speed which preliminary scientific data are being turned into tests. They should also understand the risks to patients of being stigmatised as 'susceptible' by insurers or employers, as well as the physchological and social risks patients run by putting excessive faith in predicitons of an often very uncertain future (Hubbard & Lewontin, 1996).

Uncertain future

There are many different scenarios for the future impact of genetics, and it is impossible to predict which one will prevail. As Klein has observed:

> Trying to predict the future of health policy, like any other exercise in futurology, is an enterprise best avoided. The past is littered with futures that did not happen. The only certainty is that we will always be surprised (Klein, 1997).

Uncertainty about the future, however, should not be an excuse for complacency or inaction. Opinions have tended to polarise between those who enthusiastically welcome every advance in genetics as evidence of the imminent health care revolution, and those who express caution and even cynicism in the face of such claims. It is more likely that developments will occur at different rates for different diseases with different clinical implications.

It is not the aim of this report to try and guess the exact pace and nature of change that genetics may or may not bring for each type of disease. Our aim is to identify the challenges and opportunities ahead and to outline a strategy for managing this period of unpredictable change. Only time will reveal which prediction of the future role of genetics in disease is the most accurate, but the lack of a clear consensus indicates the need for policy makers to avoid being dazzled by the promise of a future that may never materialise, or left behind by changes that they failed to anticipate.

This Chapter describes the changes which may be *possible* as a result of developments in the new genetics, with the strong caveat that it is still unclear what the pace, nature and effects of these changes will be. Using clinical case studies, we highlight some of the key questions which these developments may raise for the NHS, which are the subject of more detailed discussion in later Chapters.

Future possibilities

It is useful to think of the effect of genetics on disease in four stages. Increased understanding of the genetic components of disease may lead to:

- A new way of *classifying* disease

- The possibility of earlier *detection*

- Opportunities for the *prevention* of disease

- The ability to provide better targeted and more effective *treatment*

It is important to stress once again that the above points do not necessarily go hand in hand with one another, as detecting a disease may prove to be easier than preventing or treating it. Below we consider each of these possible developments in turn, before considering the impact which genetics could have on some diseases in particular, and on the health service in general.

Classifying disease

Developments in genetics may have a profound effect on the way that diseases are diagnosed and ultimately treated. Currently, many diseases are classified according to their symptoms; essentially the observable characteristics of a condition. This is referred to as the disease *phenotype*. Describing a condition purely according to its appearance could obscure the underlying causes of many common diseases. This in turn may account for large variations in responses to treatment, since prognosis has been based on inappropriate or inadequate diagnosis (Department of Health, 1995). Increasing knowledge about the *genotype* (the genetic make-up of a cell or individual) will lead to a better understanding of the genetic contribution to disease, such as the biochemical or physiological causes of disease.

The ability to define the biochemical processes responsible for disease may allow the subdivision of heterogeneous disease such as hypertension or diabetes into discrete entities (Bell, 1998). For example, asthma is characterised by a very broad spectrum of clinical symptoms. However, recent studies have suggested that asthma not only has a genetic component but that this component itself includes an number of different asthma susceptibility genes. Once the functions of these genes are identified, we may be able to sub-type asthmatics according to the underlying mechanisms, rather than lumping them all together under the same diagnosis and treatment regime (Skyes, 1997).

Professor John Bell concludes that 'the result of these developments is that we are beginning to move to toward a refined taxonomy in medicine that is based on biochemical mechanisms and driven by genetics' (Bell, 1998). However, it is important to stress once again that Bell represents the enthusiastic school of thought that is hotly contested by others. There are complex genetic and environmental causes of disease, and it may be a long time before the role of genes are fully understood.

Earlier detection and prevention

The NHS is currently based upon a model which aims to 'diagnose and treat' a condition. (Although a recent Green Paper published by the Department of Health has attempted to shift the focus more towards prevention). Developments in genetics will allow us to test or screen for susceptibility genes long before the symptoms of disease develop in the form of genetic testing or screening programmes. In the future, genetics may increasingly move the practice of medicine towards a 'predict and prevent' model.

The first report of the Genetics Research Advisory Group set out what it saw as the benefits of genetic screening by quoting estimates that 80-85 per cent of the aetiology of schizophrenia and asthma is accounted for by genetic factors, about 60 per cent in coronary disease and about 30 per cent in peptic ulceration. These discoveries, they claimed, offer the prospect of identifying at-risk individuals, and instituting preventative measures, such as educating them about life-style changes to diminish environmentally induced expression of a disease, or monitoring for early diagnosis and treatment (Genetics Research Advisory Group, 1995a). Predictive testing raises a number of important issues for the individual, the family and the NHS, and are discussed in detail in Chapter 2.

Critics, however, have pointed out that the mere technical ability to identify risks of disease in healthy individuals should not be interpreted as a justification for doing so. There may be commercial pressures to promote testing even when it confers no health benefits and may even result in harmful, paradoxical effects, quite apart from the cost of screening (Harper & Clarke, 1997). The role of genes in disease is complex. Genetic influences interact with environmental conditions to cause disease and it is often hard to separate out the part played by each. The cause of some diseases may be wholly genetic, in others the role played by genetics will be harder to discern.

The extent to which genetics could contribute towards a preventative health care strategy must also be considered against the failure of previous attempts to change the behaviour of at risk individuals, such as smoking.

More effective, targeted treatment

Since many treatments have tended to concentrate on relieving the symptoms, rather than the causes of disease, a better understanding of disease mechanisms, as described above, could enable a more rational approach to the development of treatments and therapies. Drugs may increasingly be designed to fit the specific molecular processes involved in causing disease.

For example, a variety of different drugs are presently being used either alone or in various combinations to treat hypertension. Each is effective for some patients but none for all. Therefore, a clearer understanding of the genetic causes of disease may enable more accurate diagnosis by identifying which particular cause of hypertension (such as the way salt is handled or the nature of muscle tone) affects which patient (Department of Health, 1995). Rational drug design may also decrease side-effects, since a person's genes can affect the way their body reacts to certain drugs. For example, individuals with different acetylator genes vary in the speed at which they metabolise (acetylate) many environmental chemicals (Department of Health, 1995).

Some have claimed that this type of approach has the potential to lower health care costs, by specifically targeting treatment to those patients who would truly benefit (Welsh Health Planning Forum, 1995). Several pharmaceutical companies are already introducing genotyping in their trials to predict responses, and eventually this information may be used to decide who should be prescribed which drugs (Bell, 1998).

Sceptics, however, argue that the likely gains from such genetic targeting may be exaggerated. The process of genetic testing to determine optimal treatments may simply not be worthwhile in human or financial terms. It is likely that there will be some clinical contexts where it is worthwhile to use knowledge about a person's genetic make-up to target therapy and many others in which symptom-based therapies may be perfectly adequate and much more cost-effective.

New types of treatment

It is not only new drugs that are being developed, but new types of treatment, such as gene therapy. Gene therapy is the replacement or repair of defective genes in living cells. There are several approaches to this process:

- *Gene replacement*: removing the faulty gene and replacing it with a normal one.

- *Gene correction*: altering genes which do not work properly by correcting the coded message in their DNA.

- *Gene augmentation*: introducing a fully functional gene into a cell without first removing or changing the existing, non-functioning gene

It is important to distinguish between two possible types of gene therapy: somatic and germ-line. The vast majority of the human body is composed of somatic cells, which make up the body's tissues and organs. The only exception are those cells from which sperm and ova develop, which are called germ cells. Alterations of the genes in somatic cells should only affect the individual concerned, whereas changes to the genes of germ cells will be passed on to future generations. There is a general consensus that, at least for the time being, germ-line gene therapy is unacceptable. There are key concerns related to safety, and ethical issues arise from the fact that we may not know the full, long-term consequences of gene therapy for the descendants of treated individuals until 'too late', if the genetic modifications are transmitted. The prospect of gene therapy raises many complex but important issues, which are beyond the remit of this report.

The impact of genetics on disease – case studies

In order to highlight the different issues which potential developments in genetics may raise for the NHS, it is useful to consider the possible impact that genetics will have upon particular diseases and with what effect. Below we outline a few case studies, before identifying some of the issues which these examples may raise for the health service. These case studies are not meant to be exhaustive, but indicative of some of the challenges ahead. We will refer to some of these case studies throughout the report.

Box 1.2 – Huntington's disease

Huntington's disease is a degenerative condition of the central nervous system that generally develops in middle age (Marteau and Richards 1996). This is a late onset single gene disorder which causes both mental and physical disability in adult life and is eventually fatal. No effective cure has been developed, although testing (presymptomatic) for the single gene is relatively straight forward. If a person is found to have the gene for Huntington's, then they have a 99 per cent chance of developing the disease. The majority of people informed about the availability currently decide not to have it done. It is generally expected that demand for the test will remain limited and only increase at a steady and moderate pace.

However, the case of Huntington's may not be comparable with other gene disorders, where testing may reveal more uncertain information. The impact of genetics on the rare single gene disorders will probably depend upon whether we develop the capacity to do something positive with the information.

Issues for the health service

- Should the NHS provide presymptomatic tests when there is no prospect of cure?

- Is the reduction of patient uncertainty and anxiety a valid outcome?

- What will the level of patient demand for such tests be?

- How (if at all) can our experience of tests for single gene disorders help us plan for the increasing availability of tests for multifactorial disorders?

Box 1.3 – Breast cancer

Three major breast cancer susceptibility genes have now been identified: *BRCA1*, *BRCA2* and p53. As with Hereditary Non-Polyposis Colon Cancer (HNPCC), *BRCA* gene testing involves identifying the small Mendelian subgroup at genuinely increased risk of disease buried within the much larger group of those who develop the disease without any specific genetic predispostion. *BRCA1* and *BRCA2* are between them responsible for approximately five per cent of all breast cancers.

Genetic prediction is only possible in cases where a predisposing mutation has been clearly identified in the family, and other family members can be tested to determine whether or not they have inherited it. Perhaps 20 per cent of mutations in *BRCA1* and *BRCA2* are missed with current techniques. The breast cancer genes are very large genes and the mutations can be individual to a family group. At the moment this is a very expensive and item consuming process, although chip technology and automated processes in the future may accelerate and simplify this process.

At present there is little formal scientific evidence to suggest how best to manage women at low, medium or high risk of developing breast cancer. The use of current interventions, such as mastectomy, is largely unproved. It is anticipated that the genetics of *BRCA1* and *BRCA2* will only play a small part in the overall management of the at risk population. Most familial cases are due to as yet unidentified environmental-genetic interactions associated with mutations or polymorphism's of low penetrance, for which no advantage would be gained from specialist genetic referrals or genetic testing. However, public awareness of and demand for the test for this gene is increasing (Zimmern, 1998a).

Issues for the health service

● Who should be offered genetic testing for the *BRCA1/2* gene and who should decide?

● Will the information provided by the test be of benefit to women and their families?

● Will the provision of testing increase demands for more interventions and counselling on the NHS?

● How can we manage inappropriate demand for this high profile genetic test?

● How can we ensure that inherited breast cancers do not receive undue attention or resources at the expense of the majority of cases (95 per cent) which have a more complex aetiology?

Box 1.4 – Cardiovascular disease (CVD)

Some types of cardiovascular disease have been shown to have a genetic component. The difficulty is in assessing what that component is and how to use the knowledge. This case study serves as an excellent illustration of the complex interaction between the genetic causes of disease and environmental conditions. Bell has suggested that there is no reason why risk factors based on DNA should not be treated in the same way as high blood pressure, which also shows incomplete penetrance and has been used for population screening (Bell, 1998).

However, the genetic variations which lie behind a particular phenotype (symptom) are so varied that finding the particular genotype may not tell us much. In familial hyper-cholesterolaemia, a similar phenotype may have 181 genotypes. The resources spent on identifying a particular genotype may therefore not translate into a clinical utility. Interventions for CVD may still depend upon measuring things like blood pressure and cholesterol levels (Welsh Health Planning Forum, 1995).

Issues for the health service

● Could/should genetics alter clinical practice?

● Will our ability to identify the particular genotype associated with a disease translate into a clinical utility?

● How will genetic services and the public respond to diseases such as CVD where there is a degree of uncertainty not found in Huntington's disease?

Box 1.5 – Thrombosis

Women with a mutant variation known as the Factor V-Leiden gene are 50 times more likely to suffer a thrombosis while taking the contraceptive pill. A test for the gene was developed in Holland three years ago and research at the University of Maastricht has found it could help identify the four per cent of mainly Caucasian women who have an increased genetic risk of deep-vein thrombosis while taking the contraceptive pill.

But some health experts have argued that it would be better not to screen any women – even those in high-risk groups, for fear of repeating the 1995 panic when thousands of British women were frightened into stopping taking the contraceptive Femodene. Dr Trevor Baglin, a consultant haematologist at Addenbrokes Cambridge has argued: 'I am completely opposed to any screening. Even if a woman does have the gene, it does not mean that she is going to develop thrombosis. You have to set the risk that she may develop a thrombosis against the effect on her life on an unwanted pregnancy. On balance it is better not to screen' (*The Observer*, 1997a).

Issues for the health service

● Which risks (and in whom) should we screen for?

● How can we compare and measure different kinds of risks?

● How do professional and lay perceptions of risks differ?

Box 1.6 – Cystic fibrosis

The most common genetic test for carrier status is for the cystic fibrosis (CF) gene. One in 25 people in Britain will be carriers of this gene, and this has led some to call for the introduction of population wide screening programmes. There is no cure for CF but it is argued that a screening programme would allow informed reproductive choices to be made.

Recent studies have indicated that prognosis may be improved by early diagnosis (Conway, 1998). Early diagnosis also takes away the period of uncertainty and anxiety for parents with an ill child and should also give opportunity for genetic counselling and pre-natal diagnosis in the next pregnancy.

Issues for the health service

- Should population screening be introduced for CF?

- How will ordinary people understand their risk status, and what will they do with the information?

- Is there a danger of creating stigmatisation or low self esteem by identifying carriers?

- Is the making of informed reproductive decisions an appropriate goal for either genetic screening programmes in particular or the NHS as a whole?

Box 1.7 – The importance of counselling

It is widely accepted that the technology of predictive genetic testing has outstripped our pyschological understanding of the impact of such testing. Whatever the result, there may be some doubt about the reliability of a genetic test, or it may not be conclusive, and may require interpretation by a trained genetic counsellor. Genetic counselling is defined as 'a communication process which deals with the occurance or risk of occurrence, of a genetic disorder in a family' (Genetics Research Advisory Group, 1995b). Others, such as Peter Harper have claimed that counselling should be considered as part of the genetic test process, and argue that genetic testing must be looked at as an overall process and not simply as a laboratory activity (Harper, 1998a).

As the Group pointed out, 'The availability of appropriate information (what to say) is an important issue but different from 'how and when to say' and 'by whom it should be said' (Genetics Research Advisory Group, 1995b). There are very real opportunities for misunderstanding and damage can easily be done to individuals who misinterpret risk data. Who should assist the patient in interpreting the result – a nurse, a GP, or a geneticist? These issues are discussed more in Chapter 4 and Chapter 7, and have been considered in detail by many other writers, such as Marteau and Richards (1996).

Issues for the health service

● Who should provide counselling and how?

● Who should have access to counselling and when?

● How should we measure counselling as an intervention?

The need for a coherent strategy

For each of these diseases, the anticipated costs and benefits of the new genetics are different, and the likelihood and timescale of developments varies. Ethical considerations as well as practical and financial will affect the pace with which tests for such diseases are introduced. These case studies reveal how vital it is for the NHS to begin to consider and debate now how it is going to respond to the challenges and changes ahead.

In its first annual report, the Human Genetics Advisory Commission (HGAC) noted:

> Genetics is a fast moving area where what may merely be a research project one year might have practical applications the next (HGAC, 1998).

It is essential that the NHS is able to anticipate developments and work flexibly and responsively towards ensuring that we can benefit from the opportunities offered. Without a strategy, genetic services could be developed in an *ad hoc* manner, subject to the demands of patients, fuelled by industrial and media interests, dependent upon the attitudes and knowledge of individual doctors and obstructed by cash strapped and short sighted health authorities.

In the following chapters, we explore in greater detail the challenges which the new genetics will raise for the health service, and consider ways of ensuring that the NHS remains in the driving seat of change.

Endnote

1   It is important to note that these numbers are not fixed, biologically-determined 'facts', but apply to specific populations at a specific period in their history. The heritibility of a trait is the proportion of the variance in the relevant phenotypic character that can be accounted for by genetic variation – and if the environment alters significantly then the heritability will also change. For example, if everyone smoked, then lung cancer would be seen as an essentially genetic trait with a high heritibility – in fact, risk of lung cancer at the population level is still much more determined by behaviour than by genetic factors.

2. Which genetic services should be provided and why?

New techniques in genetics have made it possible to identify and isolate specific genes involved in important human disorders. Genetic testing and screening programmes are now technically feasible, which may increase possibilities for accurate risk prediction or diagnosis of diseases (Advisory Committee on Genetic Testing, 1998). As the technology develops, questions for the NHS include *how, when* and *why* which kind of genetic tests or screening programmes should actually be introduced into the health service, who should make these decisions, and according to what criteria.

John Bell, writing in the *BMJ* has warned:

> .. the pressure from patients and doctors for screening services is likely to steadily increase ...There is a possibility that DNA diagnostics and pharmacogenomics will be used without proper evaluation – especially as few resources are available for rigorous evaluation and pressure continues to introduce this information in routine clinical practice (Bell, 1998).

The purpose of this chapter is to explain the different types of genetic tests and screening programmes that are, or soon maybe, technically feasible, and to identify the issues which should be considered before their widespread introduction into the health service. Our aim is to highlight the particular problems and issues which the new genetics raise that are distinct from other kinds of health care interventions. This chapter assesses how these decisions are currently made, by whom and according to what criteria and identifies the key challenges ahead for the health service.

Do the new genetics require a different response?

New technologies are being introduced into the health service every day. The Government has promised to set up a National Institute for Clinical Excellence (NICE) to help assess and manage the introduction of new technologies into the NHS (Department of Health, 1997). NICE will produce and disseminate clinical guidelines based on relevant evidence about clinical and cost-effectiveness (Department of Health, 1997). Why, if at all, should policy makers and health care professionals pay particular attention to developments in the new genetics?

There are three aspects to this question. First, there is the contentious issue of whether genetic tests are different from other forms of medical tests. This is discussed on page 86. There is then the question of how (if at all) genetic information differs from other medical or personal information. This is discussed on page 87. Finally, there is the question of whether the NHS as currently organised is capable of managing the introduction of this fast moving and high profile technology. Below we set out briefly why the NHS cannot and should not assess the new problems raised by genetics in the traditional way.

Firstly, the gap between the discovery of a test for a gene and implementation of the test is very much shorter than in any other area of health technology. This is partly due to pressure from clinicians, industry and patients (Welsh Health Planning Forum, 1995). Problems are already being experienced by those who provide services for identifying the breast cancer gene *BRCA1* and *BRCA2*, where Consultants have reported an increase in requests to be tested for the gene, following extensive media coverage (Zimmern, 1998a).

Secondly, unlike new drugs, genetic tests do not have to be approved by the Medicines Controls Agency in order to gain a licence. This narrows the interface between research and practice, and is discussed in greater detail in Chapter 5.

Thirdly, the possibility of widespread population testing and screening for susceptibility genes for common multifactorial diseases raises issues of which the health service has little experience. Criteria developed for testing and screening programmes which are used to identify the early stages of a disease may not be appropriate for a technique which may indicate the probability of a healthy person becoming ill sometime in the future. The criteria which NICE is expected to use may be too narrow for assessing the new genetic tests and screening programmes.

Finally, the lack of knowledge and experience of genetics at a primary care level, combined with the high expectations and demands of the public and the claims of industry, may encourage inappropriate referrals for genetic tests and screening programmes. The NHS may find itself pushed prematurely into a pattern of provision which is not supported by the evidence. There is already a great deal of variation in the provision of genetic testing services for breast cancer throughout the UK. Many referrals are inappropriate and there is no agreed strategy for dealing with the situation.

In order to enable the NHS to develop a coherent strategy for the introduction of genetic tests and screening programmes, several questions need to be addressed. What level and kind of accuracy should the NHS require before agreeing to fund genetic tests and screening programmes? Is it appropriate to provide a test for a disease if there is no cure? How should the NHS respond to public demand for tests of limited benefit? Should tests be provided on a population basis or targeted at those already considered at high risk? Will genetic screening programes result in more harm than benefit? What is the overall aim of genetic services?

In this Chapter we describe the different opportunities for genetic testing and screening for disease which may be available both now and in the future. Referring to the case studies outlined in Chapter 1, we draw attention to the questions which will need to be considered and debated in order to ensure that genetic services develop in the public interest.

Genetic testing and screening

The Nuffield Council on Bioethics made the following distinction between genetic testing and genetic screening:

> The phrases 'genetic testing' and genetic screening are sometimes used interchangeably. There is, however, a significant difference, *though not a completely hard and fast one*, between testing an individual for a condition or defect that other evidence suggests may be present, and screening all members of a population for a defect or condition where there is no prior evidence of its presence in the individual (Nuffield Council of Bioethics, 1993).

Within both of these categories, tests can be applied pre-natally, neo-natally, in childhood or adulthood, depending upon the nature of the disease which is being tested for. As an example of genetic tests, the Council cites testing for the Huntington's gene in the limited number of families known to be at high risk of developing the disease because they have an affected member. As an example of genetic screening, the Council cites the screening of all newborn children for phenylketonuria (PKU). Testing of a sub-population, they explain, such as Ashkenazi Jews for the Tay-Sachs gene, can also be regarded as screening.

There are different types of genetic tests and screening programmes, used for different types of diseases. Each raises a different set of questions and dilemmas, with different policy implications, which we draw attention to below.

Genetic testing

Peter Harper has suggested the following working definition of genetic testing:

> Genetic testing is the analysis of a specific gene, its product or function, or other DNA and chromosome analysis, to detect or exclude an alteration likely to be associated with a genetic disorder (Harper, 1997a).

There are two main types of genetic tests, *diagnostic* and *predictive*. Diagnostic gene testing is performed in a symptomatic individual to aid in the diagnosis, treatment and management of the patient. The use of genetic techniques in ordinary diagnosis, (the classification of a condition *after* it has begun to manifest itself), offers few problems and may, if it leads to more accurate classification and hence more effective treatment of diseases, have great benefits. Predictive testing, however, does raise some new issues for the health service, and it this aspect of the new genetics which we shall focus on.

There are essentially two types of predictive testing:
Presymptomatic tests are carried out for genetic mutations associated with dominantly inherited conditions, where having the mutation inevitably leads to the disease (this is called 'complete penetrance'). Huntington's disease is one example of this type of test, where a postitive result means that the person has a 99 per cent chance of developing the disease.

Predispositional tests are carried out for gene mutations that confer an increased risk, but not a certainty, of developing a disease. For example breast or ovarian cancer.

Current and future provision of genetic tests

The majority of predictive genetic tests currently provided are associated with reproduction. These tests provide information about the chances of genetic disorders in future children, such as testing parents to see whether they carry the gene responsible for cystic fibrosis. However, predictive tests which give people information about their *own* chances of developing a disease are becoming more common (Marteau & Croyle, 1998).

Predictive genetic tests of this kind have mainly concentrated on single gene disorders of dominant inheritance, and have therefore been of the *presymptomatic* variety. They tend to take place within the context of a family history of a disorder, with healthy relatives already aware of their genetic risk, who request tests to provide them with more information. These disorders are usually relatively uncommon, but can amount to several thousand cases. Examples include adult polycystic kidney disease, Huntington's disease, and familial polyposis of the colon. A few late onset disorders follow 'recessive' inheritance, such as haemochromatosis (Marteau & Croyle, 1998).

However, *predispostional* tests are currently being developed for the more common disorders, which are increasingly recognised as having a significant genetic component. It has been claimed that predispositional testing is set to become the main type of genetic test offered in the near future, as genes predisposing to common diseases such as cancer, Alzheimer's disease, heart disease and diabetes continue to be discovered (Marteau & Croyle, 1998). Below we consider the different issues raised by these two types of predictive tests.

Issues raised by the introduction of pre-symptomatic testing

Although the NHS has some experience of pre-symptomatic testing, this has mostly been restricted to diseases which developed in childhood. Experience of genetic testing for late onset (adult) disorders is limited, and is restricted to a small number of genetic disorders such as Huntington's disease (Marteau & Croyle, 1998). As Peter Harper has warned, 'the delivery of a service of presymptomatic genetic testing for late-onset diseases creates a series of challenges if we are to avoid inappropriate use and serious harm to those involved' (Harper, 1997b).

Which diseases should we test for and why?

Should we carry out presymptomatic tests (which by their nature are accurate) for diseases because they are common, because they are serious, because there is something clinically valid which we can do about it, or because a patient wants it? In the case of Huntington's disease, the NHS currently funds tests which can identify with 99 per cent certainty whether or not a person will develop this fatal disease, but there is still no hope of a cure. A positive test could be devastating for an individual and his or her family, but a negative test may alleviate anxiety. The dilemmas which such tests raise for the individual and families concerned are illustrated in a series of personal accounts in the *The Troubled Helix* (Marteau and Richards, 1996).

What if scientists continue to develop technologies which allow us to identify the genes involved in diseases which we have no ability to prevent or treat? Is there any point in providing such tests? Some commentators, such as Professor Eve Johnstone, have argued that it would not be helpful for a person to learn that they may develop a disease before they die, particularly if there is no treatment available (House of Commons Select Committee on Science and Technology, or HCSCST, 1995). Others, however, may feel that such information could enable a person to make important financial or reproductive choices about their life. This issue points to the need to be clear about the aims of genetic services, which is discussed in greater detail below.

What will be the level of public demand for such tests? Will people prefer to remain uncertain about the future? The take up rate for the test for Huntington's disease is currently only about 10 per cent, although this could change dramatically of we develop the ability to treat this fatal disease. Levels of demand are also likely to be influenced by whether insurance companies or employers have access or not to the results of such tests. This is discussed in greater detail in Chapter 6.

When should such tests be provided?

Because presymptomatic testing provides the patient with almost certain knowledge of their future health status, the question of when to perform the test is an important one, particularly if the disease is of late-onset. Should it be carried out pre-natally, in early childhood or only in adult life? Who should decide?

It could be helpful to test young children in families of high risk to alleviate parental anxiety, or where early medical intervention could prevent or improve later symptoms. However, if the disease is of late-onset and incurable, the postitive testing of a child could have damaging consequences (Clarke, 1997a) Concern has been expressed that presymptomatic testing on young children, at the request of parents, will infringe the child's right not to know of their later health status. It is important to point out that even if a person tests positive for Huntington's disease, we have no way of knowing at what age it will strike and with what degree of severity.

If a (currently) well person has a presymptomatic test which reveals that they will (eventually) suffer from an incurable disease, how does this affect their status? Are they are a patient, a healthy person, or will we need to develop a new category to describe this grey area? What impact will such knowledge have on other NHS resources such as counselling services and primary care teams, who may have to respond to the needs of 'the worried well'?

Issues raised by the introduction of predispostional testing

The anticipated growth in the availability of predispostional testing for multifactorial diseases will present the NHS with major challenges:

> For the common 'multifactorial' disorders there is almost no experience in a service setting since the range of specific genes and environmental factors involved has rarely been sufficiently established to allow accurate prediction ...Data are now becoming available from some forms of familial cancer but there is an urgent need for such data to be collected on other late onset disorders (Advisory Committee on Genetic Testing, 1998).

When should such tests be provided and why?

What use could be made of the information provided by predispositional tests and how well do we understand it? In the case of breast cancer, when the mutation is identified within a family then those who carry the mutation are deemed to have an 80 per cent lifetime risk of developing breast cancer. This means that 20 per cent will not develop breast cancer as a result of carrying the risk mutation, although we do not yet know why. In most other multifactorial diseases, we cannot even quantify, let alone explain, the probability of a person developing the disease. The relationship between genes and the environment is just too complex.

What could or should be done with the information provided by predispostional tests? In the case of breast cancer, there is, at present, little that can be done to prevent or treat this disease, even if the *BRCA1/BRAC2* gene is identified. The use of current interventions such as mammography is largely unproved. A number of trials have given failure rates of 15–19 per cent for prophylactic surgery, and although it is probably effective at reducing risk in very high risk women, the risk is not reduced to zero (Zimmern, 1998a).

However, as the technology for testing for susceptibility to multifactorial disorders becomes available, the opportunities for preventative care may become apparent for some diseases, particularly those with a strong environmental or life style component. For example, identifying the gene for maturity onset diabetes in the young known as MODY will make dietary and therapeutic intervention possible in the at risk group. However, it is questionable whether patients who are told of their increased risk for developing a particular disease will adapt their behaviour accordingly. Some may respond in a fatalistic manner, and perversely increase, rather than reduce, the risk factors in their life.

To whom should such tests be provided and why?

If the NHS did provide predispositional genetic tests, who should undergo such tests? Should the NHS test those at low, medium or high risk of developing a disease, how should these categories be defined and by whom? In the case of breast cancer, it has been suggested that only those deemed to be of high risk should be offered genetic tests. It has been estimated that in a population of one million, around 20 to 40 high risk families would be eligible for mutation testing for breast cancer. However, there appears to be no national consensus about what constitutes 'high risk' (Zimmern, 1998a) although some progress has been made (Post, 1997).

How do we allay the concerns of those deemed to be 'low' or medium' risk, and ensure that they are managed appropriately? Clinical and lay views on degrees of risk may differ significantly (Marteau and Richards, 1996). Will women who perceive themselves to be at risk be driven into the private sector in search of knowledge and reassurance that the NHS will not provide? The issue of commercial testing is discussed in Chapter 5.

Current guidelines for genetic tests

The Conservative government acknowledged the need to address the particular issues raised by developments in genetic testing by establishing the Advisory Committee on Genetic Testing (ACGT) in July 1996. The terms of reference are:

●   To provide advice to Ministers on developments in testing for genetic disorders

●   To advise on testing individuals for genetic disorders, taking account of ethical, social and scientific aspects; and

●   To establish requirements, especially in respect of efficacy and product information, to be met by manufacturers and suppliers of genetic tests

The ACGT has produced a Code of Practice for genetic testing offered commercially to the public (see Chapter 5) and have recently published a consultation report to guide the introduction of late onset genetic tests which will apply both to the public and private sector (ACGT, 1998). The work of the ACGT in general and the consultation report on genetic testing in particular is invaluable, and will be of great help to health professionals and policy makers in the forthcoming years.

In their consultation report on genetic tests for late onset disorders, the ACGT lists a range of considerations which should be made before introducing genetic tests as a service. The prime concern of the ACGT appears to be that the scientific and clinical validity of the test should be established before putting into practice (ACGT, 1998). The report draws attention to the importance of establishing the extent and limitation of the association between the test result and the disorder, the error and failure rate, and the quality of the laboratories undertaking the genetic test.

These criteria seem wise and appropriate, but it is perhaps disappointing that the consultation report of the ACGT does not refer to or discuss other potential criteria, such as the severity of the disease, the ability to do something clinically valid with the result, or indeed, the aims of genetic tests in general.

The consultation report of the ACGT is primarily concerned only with late onset single gene disorders; that is, presymptomatic testing. Presymptomatic testing of young children for disorders not currently influenced by therapy or of late-onset is not recommended. In Annex C the report outlines the issues raised by testing for genetic susceptibility. The report suggest the following reasons for identifying genetic susceptibilities:

- Aid understanding of disease mechanisms

- Aid drug choice and dosage

- Help target immunisation and related programmes

- Allow lifestyle changes to reduce risk factors

The ACGT conclude that any evidence that predispostional testing will give any of the above benefits remains preliminary. Peter Harper has suggested elsewhere that genetic testing for susceptibilities to common diseases is not justified at present (Welsh Institute for Health and Social Care, 1998).

Suggested criteria for the introduction of genetic tests

The recent consultation report by the ACGT has been extremely useful in putting these issues on the agenda for debate. This document, combined with other literature in the field quoted above, points to an emerging consensus on the criteria which should guide the current introduction of genetic tests in the NHS at this stage. We have attempted to summarise and describe this emerging consensus below:

- Tests should be scientifically and clinically valid – at present most predispositional tests would not appear to be justified

- Tests should only be offered to families known to be at high risk

- Results should enable a positive intervention or improved management to be made[1]

- Presymptomatic testing of children should ordinarily not be provided

- Tests should only be offered where is adequate provision for information and counselling to be given pre- and post- testing.

It would seem appropriate to use this criteria as a *starting point* only. Experience of genetic tests in the health service is too low at the moment to warrant any rigid guidelines, and the desire for coherence must be balanced with the need to avoid restricting progress. Genetics is a fast moving area of science, and as we shall see in the following Chapters, changes in the organisation and delivery of health services in the UK require policy makers to avoid setting 'best practice' prematurely in stone and to remain capable of responding to the constant and unpredictable changes ahead.

It is likely that different genetic conditions and tests will require different criteria and guidelines. This points to the need to monitor and evaluate the current provision of genetic tests and screening programmes so that we can continue to learn from different models of service provision, and identify best practice. This is discussed in more detail on p40.

Issues raised by genetic screening programmes

Increasing knowledge and developments in technology allows genetic tests to be used for screening large groups, even whole populations for the detection of late onset disorders, such as cystic fibrosis, Tay-Sachs disease, sickle cell anaemia and Thalassaemia. However, just because a service is technically possible, this does not mean that the NHS should provide it. The use of genetic tests for screening raises important issues over and above those for family based genetic testing. Those being screened will be likely to know less about the disorder, the test and the implications in the absence of a family history. Population screening programmes can be expensive, and may raise as well as reduce anxiety in many people.

Angus Clarke, a consultant clinical geneticist, has written extensively on the issues raised by genetic screening programmes. He points out that the key difference between family-based genetic tests and population-based screening is that the former involves responding to concerns that are already there, whereas the latter raises concerns that may not otherwise exist. Because of the potential for harm, he warns that it is important to carefully weigh up the benefits before offering wide spread genetic screening programmes (Harper & Clarke, 1997)

The issues raised by genetic screening will depend upon which types of screening programme is being carried out, at which point in the life cycle, and for what purpose. Below we draw on the work of Angus Clarke to help separate out the issues which genetic screening will raise for health care professionals and policy makers.

Newborn screening

The development of newborn screening, according to Angus Clarke, is one of the great success stories of twentieth century preventative medicine (Clarke, 1997b). He cites the example of phenylketonuria (PKU) which affects about one child in every 10, 000 in Britain. It causes severe intellectual impairment, but its ill effects can largely be prevented if an affected child follows a low protein diet soon after birth. Screening such as this meets the World Health Organisation guidelines for the adoption of screening programmes (Wilson & Junger, 1968) and raises few new issues for policy makers where an early diagnosis is known to be of benefit to the child. If the disease screened for, however, were to be of late-on-set, with no clear clinical interventions, then it would raise the same problems as identified in genetic testing for children on page 31, where a child's right not to know about their future health status could be infringed, with devastating pyschological effects.

Genetic screening for carrier status

This type of screening attempts to identify those who carry faulty genes, which will not affect them, but may be passed on to their children.[2] The most common genetic test for carrier status is for the cystic fibrosis (CF) gene. One in 25 people in Britain will be carriers of this gene, and this has led some to call for the introduction of population wide screening programmes. There is no cure for CF but it is argued that a screening programme would allow informed reproductive choices to be made.

This raises a number of issues. Being identified as a carrier may result in stigmatization or low self esteem for some people. What is informed choice to one person may seem like a series of burdens to another. How will ordinary people understand their risk status, and what will they do with the information?

More importantly, can the making of informed reproductive decisions be regarded as an appropriate goal for either genetic screening programmes in particular or the NHS as a whole? Will such screening in the context of a cash-strapped health service genuinely offer undirected choice? There may be inappropriate pressure put on couples to abort affected babies, as a child with cystic fibrosis can be costly to care for. Would couples end up undergoing a test that they otherwise would not have chosen and making 'choices' which they might otherwise not have made? Clarke draws attention to the variable uptake of CF testing, warning of 'apathy and compliance in the face of professional enthusiasm' (Clarke, 1997c).

Carrier screening illustrates the need to be clear about what the aims of genetic services are, and to remain aware of the impact that such screening programmes could have at an individual and societal level. Unlike other screening programmes, it is not enough to just consider issues of accuracy or clinical effectiveness, as there are important ethical issues involved. These issues are discussed in greater detail in Chapter 3.

Genetic screening for susceptibility genes

It is anticipated that there will be significant growth in the availability of predispositional genetic testing for susceptibility genes. Should or could this lead to population screening for such genes in the future? The justification for such screening programmes, could, like testing, be the potential for those 'at risk' to alter their life style.

First, there are likely to be problems with validity and perception of the risk estimate. We do not yet understand the relationship between genes and the environment in multifactorial diseases. Secondly, it is unclear how lay perceptions of risk will differ from professional assessments, and thirdly, how (if at all) this would affect their behaviour.

The failure of many people to reduce known risk factors such as drinking and smoking is well documented. Indeed, some may even react in a fatalistic way, exacerbating their risk factors (Clarke, 1997c). What impact would such screening programmes have on other public health measures? There is a danger that such screening could over-emphasise the role of the individual and 'internal' risks, reducing public and political pressure for tackling 'external' risks to health, such as pollution.

Prenatal genetic screening

This type of screening offers pregnant women the opportunity to know the future health status of their foetus. This is perhaps the most controversial of all genetic screening programmes, as it forces us to confront and discuss exactly what the aims of any screening programme might be. Clarke has identified three established reasons for justifying prenatal screening: sparing resources through the termination of affected pregnancies, the avoidance of suffering in affected children through termination and the promotion of informed reproductive choices (Clarke, 1997d). Each of these, he claims is problematic, and again points to the need to define the aims of genetic services. The introduction of genetic screening programmes will have repercussions beyond the individual who is tested. What will it say about our society if we screen all foetuses for Down's syndrome or spina bifida, (rather than, as at present, just those families deemed to be at high risk)? How would people currently affected by these conditions feel if a widespread screening programme was introduced? These issues are considered further in Chapter 3.

Current guidelines for genetic screening

There is as yet no body with a remit to consider the introduction of genetic screening in the UK. A National Screening Committee (NSC) was set up in 1996 by the Department of Health to oversee all national population screening programmes, but their remit and expertise does not include genetics. The terms of reference of the NSC are:

●   On the basis of sound evidence to advise DoH, CMO, the Wider DoH and the NHS Executive Board of the timeliness and appropriateness of implementation, development, review, modification and where necessary, the cessation of screening programmes.

- To advise Ministers, the Chief Medical Officer, the NHS Research & Development Programme and DoH, on the need for research reviews and analytical work to help focus and make best use of research.

- Through the programme specific Advisory Groups and others, to monitor and be advised of the progress, problems and research needs of ongoing NHS screening programmes and where appropriate, advise on standards and monitoring arrangements (Department of Health, 1996).

The NSC has developed a specification for population screening, created a national inventory of screening and developed criteria for appraising the screening programme (Department of Health, 1998a) In a handbook for NHS professionals, the NSC sets out two pages of criteria that should ideally be met before screening for a condition is initiated. To summarise, the committee decided that:

- The condition should be an important health problem

- The test should be simple, safe, valid and precise

- There should be an effective treatment or intervention, with evidence of better outcomes as a result

- There should be evidence that the screening programme is effective in reducing mortality or morbidity.

Criteria for genetic screening

The above criteria is aimed at all types of health screening programmes, but how appropriate is this as a guide to the introduction of genetic screening? Health professionals may have different aims for and concerns about genetic screening programmes, that lead to a different set of questions not addressed by the above criteria. The Nuffield Council on Bioethics produced a comprehensive report on the issue of genetic screening in 1993, where they suggested the following criteria should be used to guide the introduction of genetic screening programmes:

- The aims and purposes of the entire programme

- The predictive power and level of accuracy of the particular screening test

- The value to those being screened of the knowledge gained

- The availability of therapy for the particular condition, accepting that lack of treatment does not necessarily mean that screening is not worthwhile

- The potential social implications

- The resource costs

A careful review will be required of the more difficult ethical considerations arising from future genetic screening programmes ... the introduction of such programmes should be subject to stringent review ... each condition [will] need to be separately reviewed. This is because each may give rise to particular ethical problems depending upon the nature of the condition, its severity, its variability and its likely onset (Nuffield Council of Bioethics, 1993).

It is clear that criteria developed for testing and screening programmes which are used to identify the early stages of a disease are not sufficient to address the issues raised by techniques which may indicate the probability of a healthy person becoming ill sometime in the future.

However, the criteria generated by the National Screening Committee and the Nuffield Council of Bioethics respectively provide a useful basis for a debate about the appropriate introduction of screening for particular genetic conditions. The NCB originally recommended that the Department of Health should set up a central coordinating body to review genetic screening programmes and monitor their implementation and outcome. The National Screening Committee (NSC) has no specific remit to look at genetic screening, but is not prevented from doing so. It has good links with the Advisory Committee on Genetic tests, which does have an expertise in genetics, although they do not look at screening issues.

Review of current decision-making mechanisms

One of the biggest problems facing policy makers in the field of genetics is the lack of accurate and quality data on what services are currently being provided and with what effect. The National Screening Committee has undertaken an inventory of over 300 screening programmes, and it has a duty to monitor continually the effectiveness, quality and management of the overall performance of screening programmes. This is a welcome development.

However, these duties are not shared by the Advisory Committee on Genetic Testing, whose prime responsibility is to advise on the future provision of genetic testing. Whilst the forward looking work of the ACGT is invaluable, there is also a need to collate and assess information on the extent and effects of tests which are actually being provided at present. This knowledge gap means that policy is in danger of developing on the basis of inadequate data and a mixture of prejudices and presuppositions.

There is an urgent need to:

● *Monitor* current provision of genetic services (testing and screening)

● *Evaluate* different models of provision

● *Disseminate* best practice and guidelines

The Conservative Government reacted to calls for a national co-ordinated strategy to deal with issues raised by genetics in an *ad hoc* and incoherent way. In the space of less than a year, they created the National Screening Committee, the Advisory Committee on Genetic Testing and the Human Genetics Advisory Commission. Including the Gene Therapy Advisory Group, we now have four bodies looking at different aspects of genetic services in the NHS.

Both the Advisory Committee on Genetic Testing and the National Screening Committee have made an impressive contribution towards resolving dilemmas raised by the new genetics, and their roles are continuing to evolve. The various committees and commissions on genetics in the UK provide Government with an invaluable source of expert advice and knowledge. The committees have often produced some excellent work, under difficult circumstances and with few resources to support them. However, it is worth considering whether the current arrangements are working as effectively as they might be, and whether there are any important issues which are currently not being addressed, or indeed, are being duplicated.

The potential for a lack of co-ordination has been reduced by the recent introduction of informal mechanisms to ensure that the ACGT and the NSC communicate with each other. This is a welcome beginning, but efforts must be continued to ensure that communications develop as effectively as possible, both horizontally (between committees and departments) and vertically (upwards to NHS Executive and Ministers and downwards to and up from providers and users of services on the ground).

Committees such as the ACGT have members who are selected for their expertise, such as clinical geneticists and GPs. There is no public health perspective on the ACGT, although this is vital if the committee is to consider the future development of genetics within the wider context of the NHS. The National Screening Committee, on the other hand, has plenty of members with public health expertise, but nobody with a background in genetics. The NSC has an enormous remit, as some of the programmes up and running are beset by problems, where sensitivity, specitivity, uptake and access are all a problem. There are perhaps different ethical issues surrounding the introduction of genetic screening programmes, which may beyond their capacity.

It is therefore essential that the two bodies continue to share their expertise. Just as important, the relevant departments within the NHS should share and implement relevant information. For example, the recent report from the ACGT on genetic testing for late onset disorders has important implications for the number, training and education of future NHS staff and clinicians.

As a total of four bodies concerned with different aspects of genetic tests and screening were created in 1996, it would now seem appropriate to initiate a short but multi-disciplinary review into how effectively these bodies are working, with a view to strengthening and co-ordinating their functions. It would be particularly useful to consider how (if at all) the various committees might relate or contribute to the agenda set out in the recent White Paper (Department of Health, 1997).

Summary of issues and recommendations

Criteria for genetic testing and screening

These questions raise important social and ethical issues, which cannot be separated from questions about the aim of genetic services and who should be involved in making these decisions. In the short term we recommend:

- The criteria suggested by the ACGT and the NSC provide a useful starting point for debate

- These guidelines should be interpreted in the light of each particular condition, paying particular attention to the voice of users

Review current decision making mechanisms

The aim is to build upon and strengthen existing decision making mechanisms. The last thing we need is yet another new committee or commission. Instead, we recommend that the Department of Health initiates a short but multi-disciplinary review to consider how to weave together the work of existing committees, in order to ensure greater coherence and co-ordination in the future. In particular, the review should consider:

- How to ensure greater vertical and horizontal communication between all the committees and stakeholders

- Who should be responsible for monitoring and evaluating *all* genetic services

- How to ensure the effective dissemination and sharing of best practice

- How might the committees relate and contribute to the emerging work of the National Institute for Clinical Excellence (NICE).

Endnotes

1   Positive intervention could include lifestyle choices as well as clinical interventions. Interpretation of this criteria depends upon a clarification of the aims of genetic services. This is discussed in Chapter 3.

2   There are different biological categories of carrier status. For a full discussion of these issues, see Clarke AJ (1997c) 'Population screening for genetic carrier status' in Harper and Clarke.

3. Issues for purchasers

In the previous chapters we outlined the challenges which developments in genetic knowledge will raise for the National Health Service in general. In the following two chapters, we consider the issues which the new genetics will raise for those at the coal face: the purchasers and providers of health care services.

The issue of purchasing genetic services in the NHS is yet another moving target. Just as policy makers and practitioners were beginning at least to understand, if not support, the internal market, it is being dismantled by a Labour Government committed to developing a 'third way' in the NHS (Department of Health, 1997). This is a period of continuing change, not only in the genetic services which are available but also the infrastructure which provides them. The role of purchasing, currently performed by health authorities will soon be a function of Primary Care Groups. In this chapter we discuss the key issues that genetics will raise for purchasers, highlighting the problems of the old system as well as the challenges for the new.

In order to consider how purchasers might appropriately buy genetic services, a number of key questions must first be addressed. How should we measure genetics as a service? How should we define a successful outcome? Who should be involved in these decisions? At what level should genetic services be purchased? Central to all of these issues is the key question which will confront purchasers: what is the aim of genetics? The answer to this question will determine what kind and level of genetic services are purchased in the new NHS.

What should be the aim of genetic services?

Purchasers, at whatever level, have to buy a whole range of health care services for their populations, with genetics a small (but growing) part of their budgets. It is vital that those concerned with the future provision of genetic services begin to answer the questions that purchasers will no doubt ask themselves when confronted with a request for resources: What exactly am I buying?

It is fairly clear how one would assess the clinical and cost effectiveness of a traditional intervention, such as a drug or surgery. The general aim of traditional interventions is to cure or improve the management of a disease once a person has been diagnosed as suffering from it. Purchasers can weigh up the cost of the service against the benefit gained. This is a crude simplification of a complex and controversial process, but the distinction is valid. Developments in genetics will enable us to predict the likelihood of future diseases in healthy people, sometimes (though not always) offering opportunities for disease prevention. This will require a paradigm shift in the way in which we think about and measure our health care services in the future.

It is possible to distinguish at least three different purposes or aims for genetic services: human rights, utilitarian and clinical. The future development of genetic services in the UK will depend upon which of these aims the NHS decides to sign up to.

Human rights

It is often claimed that the aim of genetic services is to enable individuals to make better informed decisions about their own health, for example, to change their lifestyle or to accept or refuse treatment. The National Screening Committee refers to this as the 'human rights' approach. (National Screening Committee, 1998). In 1991 Professor Rodney Harris gave this summary of the aims of medical genetics:

- To ensure the maximum range of options for those at risk of genetic disease by providing accurate diagnosis and screening, empathic genetic counselling and support.

- To prevent disease and unnecessary anxiety by facilitating personal informed choices from among these options.

- To aid appropriate clinical management of genetic disease and to identify preventable complications by early and accurate diagnosis (Harris, 1991).

Whilst many would agree with the sentiments behind these aims, this approach could be problematic. The choices of individuals impact upon others. This has always been true of the health service, where finite resources have meant that for every decision to treat there is an opportunity cost: Money spent on one service means that it cannot be spent elsewhere. Is it the role of a publicly-funded health service to provide people with more information about their future health status, regardless of our ability to prevent or cure a disease?

For example, if a woman received ante-natal screening for cystic fibrosis, which proved to be positive, and following counselling decided to go ahead with a pregnancy, how would purchasers measure this as an outcome? In this instance, the NHS will have enabled one individual to make an informed choice about their life, which a Consultant Clinical Geneticist would regard as a success – but what about a Director of Public Health working for a cash-strapped health authority?

Utilitarian

The aim of many screening programmes is to reduce the prevalence of the disease in the community or population as a whole. The National Screening Committee refers to this as a 'utilitarian' approach (National Screening Committee, 1998). However, it is questionable whether such an approach is appropriate for genetic services. A paper was recently produced for the NHS Executive on the experience of screening for Fragile X syndrome, a disorder characterised by a complex mixture of physical, cognitive and behavioural features (Murray & Cuckle, 1997). With regards to the objective of the screening programme, the authors quite clearly state:

> ... the principle public health aim of screening for fragile X syndrome is to reduce the birth prevalence of the disorder ...Two of the reported cascade screening programmes have estimated the average cost of preventing an affected birth as $12,740 ...This is a small fraction of the costs of care for an affected individual, which are a minimum $1 million.

Concerns have been expressed that approaches such as those outlined above could increase the stigmatisation suffered by disabled people. McLean highlights the difficulties which those who survive birth with identified genetic problems may face. The self-perception of the individual may be affected, as may other peoples' attitudes to them and indeed their parents, who could be viewed as socially irresponsible, to have proceeded with a pregnancy in the knowledge, rather than ignorance of, the consequences (McLean, 1997).

Of course, we must not forget that many people quite legitimately and understandably choose to abort rather than give birth to children who might suffer. It is also important to acknowledge that a major step towards enabling people to make genuinely free decisions about their future reproduction would be to improve the support and services for people with disabilities.

Clinical

There is a third approach which is relevant to the field of genetics, which we have chosen to call the 'clinical' approach. This view is typified by those who think that a test or screening programme should only be carried out if there is something 'clinically valid' which can be done with the information. This is distinct from the human rights approach, as in some diseases, such as Huntington's disease, we do not yet have the capacity to prevent, manage or cure this disease. The test is offered on the basis that individuals may benefit from a removal or confirmation of their anxiety, and that they have a right to both knowledge and ignorance of their future health status.

The clinical approach is also distinct from the utilitarian view, as the aim may not to prevent or reduce the incidence of disease, but to improve the managemement of those affected. For example, there is some evidence that early detection of cystic fibrosis can improve the management and prognosis of the disease, so a test for this gene could be considered clinically valid.

Again, this approach is not unproblematic. What do patients understand by the concept of valid? Is it only clinical interventions that are valid, or should we equally value the opportunity for an affected individual to make informed choices about their or their family's future? According to the clinical approach, there would be no point in testing an adult to see if he or she posesed the gene for late onset Huntington's, as there is absoloutely no cure for this fatal disease.

Some purchasers and clinicians may be unwilling to spend money on a service that only provides an individual with more information about their future health status in the absence of any clinical intervention, and may prefer to invest in services which are known to improve the health status of the population.

Aims and consequences

It is clear that the aims of genetic services is both controversial and important. The approach taken by those working in the NHS will have a profound effect on the way in which genetic services are perceived and develop. Of course, the human rights, utilitarian and clinical approaches are not watertight or mutually exclusive. In practice, we may have a combination of overlapping or conflicting aims. Indeed, it is perhaps helpful to separate out aims from consequences. The Royal College of Physicians considered the relationship between aims and consequences and concluded:

> Reductions in morbidity and mortality may become outcome measures in time but at present they remain within the remit of research. There is evidence that one consequence of the informed reproductive decisions that couples make will be a reduced prevalence of certain serious genetic disorders. But this is not a primary purpose of genetic counselling and its use as a measure of the outcomes of genetic counselling is mistaken (Royal College of Physicians, 1998).

It is useful to make the distinction between aims and consequences, and in our view, to make clear that it should not be the aim of genetic services to reduce the number of affected births. However, there is always a danger that people will use the language of rights but in practice act differently. This is similar to what ethicists have called the 'doctrine of double effect'. A commitment towards a human rights approach may be used to (cosmetically) distance the speaker from nasty 'eugenic' abuses of genetics without altering the ethos of the service on offer. For example, in a report in 1991, although the Royal College of Physicians claimed that the aim of medical genetics is 'to help those families with a genetic disadvantage to live and reproduce as normally as possible' (Royal College of Physicians, 1991), elsewhere in the report the Royal College of Physicians states:

> A further benefit of a genetic service is to reduce the birth frequency of children with chronic mental and motor handicaps with obvious benefits to individual families and

with financial savings for the community (Royal College of Physicians, 1991)

Eugenics is the doctrine which claims that it is possible and desirable, through selective breeding and the elimination of undesirable individuals, to alter the hereditary qualities of a race or population. It thus aims to improve the quality of a species rather than an individual (Nuffield Council on Bioethics, 1993). The word eugenics was devised by Sir Francis Galton, being derived from the Greek word 'eugenes' which means 'well born' or 'hereditarily endowed with noble qualities' (Macer, 1990).

The Nuffield Council on Bioethics warned that the potential for eugenic misuse of genetic testing will increase with the technology:

> This makes it all the more important for society to keep genetic screening under review and, if necessary, limit misapplications at an early stage. We must ensure that neither specific individuals, nor society as a whole, are harmed by a hasty or ill considered application of genetic testing (Nuffield Council of Bioethics, 1993).

As Harper has noted, there is a tension, both ethical and practical, between population-directed and individual-directed goals in medical genetics (Harper & Clarke, 1997). In order to prevent future problems, Harper argues that we need to distinguish between population and individual aims, and be aware of the past:

> It is easy to regard the excesses of the eugenics movement or the abuses in Nazi Germany as disconnected from present day medical genetics, but a closer look at these episodes shows that their key feature was the subordination of individual decisions to the broader population-based goals (Harper, 1997c).

However, subordinating the public good to individual choice may be equally problematic. McLean notes that the liberal Western tradition seeks to emphasise the uniqueness of the individual by valuing concepts such as autonomy and integrity. But what happens when the choices made by lots of individuals impact upon the rest of society and indeed, change the very content? What happens if the wealthy are able to buy genetic technologies in order to buy advantage for their offspring, just as they currently send them to public school? (Silvers L 1998) As Monbiot has noted,

> The dangers with which ... genetic choices confront us emerge not from the threat of the coercive state, but from the less fashionable bogey of mass consumerism. What is good for the individual may be disastrous for society. (*The Guardian*, 1997)

Elsewhere we have written of the need to develop a philosophy of citizenship, rather than consumerism in the health service. The citizens' perspective recognises that meeting the community needs can rarely be simple. There is a need to develop a 'third way' between mass consumerism and the dominance of population based goals in which the rights and needs of the individual can be fairly considered in relation to the good of the wider community (Lenaghan, 1996).

These are important issues, and require a wide and informed public debate. It is vital that we have an open and honest discussion about the purpose of genetic services, so that we can unpick some of these contradictory approaches, and where possible, strike an appropriate balance. It may be that it is possible to distinguish the consequences of a genetic service from the aims, and to embrace a sophisticated approach to public health which facilitates rather than prevents the informed choices of individuals. A greater emphasis on positively welcoming children and adults affected by genetic conditions into our society and de-emphasising the link between genetic tests and abortions would be the best way of ensuring that genetic services genuinely facilitate informed choices.

To this end, we recommend that the Human Genetics Advisory Commission (HGAC) should initiate and lead a public and professional debate on the aims of genetic services. The HGAC was established in December 1996. The terms of reference are:

- keep under review scientific progress at the frontiers of human genetics and related fields

- report on issues arising from new developments in human genetics that can be expected to have wider social, ethical and/or economic consequences of developments in human genetics, for example in relation to public health, insurance, patents and employment.

● advise on ways to build public confidence in and understanding of the new genetics

The HGAC is a non-statutory advisory body, and reports independently to the Department of Trade and Industry and the Department of Health on issues that have social, ethical and/or economic consequences. The HGAC is open to Government to seek its advice on particular issues. The HGAC has recently published its first annual report, and two consultation documents on cloning and insurance. As the aims of genetics will have wide social, ethical and economic implications, it would seem appropriate for the HGAC to put this issue high on their agenda.

How should purchasers measure genetic services?

Once the aims have been decided, there is then the difficult question of how to measure success. This issue is high on the agenda of the new Labour government, who have proposed to set up a National Institute for Clinical Excellence (NICE), to produce and disseminate guidelines on clinical and cost effectiveness, and have promised to create a new national performance framework to measure the success of the NHS (Department of Health, 1997). As noted in Chapter 2, there are concerns that the criteria and methods developed by NICE and other bodies will not be sufficient or appopriate for measuring genetic services. For example, if the NHS signed up to the 'human rights' view of genetics, how do we measure a service whose aim is to 'help people with a genetic disadvantage to live and reproduce as normally as possible'? (World Health Organisation, 1985).

The Genetic Interest Group (GIG) have argued that:

Many of the 'outcomes' of the service are difficult to measure in a traditional way. The aim is to inform the individual of their circumstances and risk factors. For the family as a whole the task may well be to reassure many members that they are not at risk, or that they have a quantifiable risk of having a child with a specific condition which might be reduced or eliminated if certain steps are followed (Genetic Interest Group, 1995a)

The Royal College of Physicians agrees that these outcomes are psychological, and difficult, if not impossible, to measure by current methods. The primary aim of genetic services such as tests or screening programmes accompanied by counselling may be to provide an individual with more information about their future health, for which there may or may not be something clinically valid which can be done, or indeed, the patient may choose *not* to take advantage of the clinical intervention available (Royal College of Physicians, 1998).

In view of the difficulties in practice of assessing the effectiveness and outcome of a genetics service, the RCP recommends that quality indicators be accepted by purchasers. The RCP proposes a number of indicators, including the scope of the service, the accessibility and responsiveness of the services and the quality of the clinical care (Royal College of Physicians, 1998). The indicators will serve as a basis of service specification. However, these indicators may help purchasers to decide between providers, but not what services to actually buy. Why should they spend money on genetic services as opposed to other competing claims on their resources?

There is, however, one aspect of genetic services which can be assessed in a fairly simple, quantitative way – by counting the number of those at high risk of complications of genetic disorders who are enrolled in a proper monitoring and surveillance programme, and counting the number of family members who are reassured that they are not at risk (despite their family history) and so do not need to take part in surveillance. These figures could be worked out for several familial cancers, Marfan syndrome and a few cardiovascular disorders, and would focus on the postitive, rather than negative outcomes of genetic services.

The traditional approach of measuring what is clinically and cost effective is clearly too narrow for the assessment of the new genetic services. Developments in genetics will present purchasers with new challenges, and it is therefore vital that we develop open, relevant and appropriate criteria to purchase genetic services. The criteria which are used to make these decisions should therefore be developed following full consultation with professionals, users and carers.

Open and explicit criteria

Whilst there is clear disagreement about the aims and criteria which should be used for measuring genetic services, there is a strong case for making whatever criteria is used open and explicit. The Genetic Interest Group have pointed out that whereas providers are constantly having to demonstrate the value of their service, there is currently no obligation upon purchasers to be open about the criteria which they use to buy genetic services, or indeed its relevance. As the ACGT has argued:

> There is a potential conflict in genetic screening programmes between the aim of maximising choice for individuals and 'public health' goals of reducing the frequency of a genetic disorder. The aims of any screening programme should be made explicit (ACGT, 1998).

It is not possible to separate the question of what the purpose of genetic services is, from the equally important issue of who should be involved in these decisions.

Multi-disciplinary approach

Harper has claimed that one of the key problems is the huge gap between those with a public health background and those with an expertise in clinical genetics. There is virtually no genetics included in the speciality of public health:

> We thus have the situation that those involved in determining public health medicine programmes, and who also have a wider influence on commissioning of health care, including genetic services, have little concept of what medical genetics as a speciality is or does (Harper, 1997c).

Harper goes on to argue for every health region to have one of its public health medicine staff interested and experienced in medical genetics, who could then have special responsibility for the population-based programmes. We need mechanisms for ensuring that geneticists and public health specialists have the opportunity to share their relevant knowledge and experience at both a local and national level. Recent proposals to allow Primary Care Group Boards to co-opt other members offer a useful starting point. (HSC, 1998)

In the next section we move from discussing how genetic services should be purchased and measured, to consider who should be taking these decisions and at what level.

Who should purchase genetic services and at what level?

In order to understand the recent proposals in the White Paper, and to consider how we might develop appropriate purchasing strategies for genetic services, it is useful to remind ourselves what existed before (and to some extent still does) and why change was thought necessary. In this way, we hope to learn from the mistakes and successes of the past and develop a successful strategy for the future.

Purchaser/provider split

In 1991 the Conservative government begin to implement a programme of radical reforms in the NHS, aimed at creating an internal market. One of the most significant changes introduced was the separation of purchaser and provider roles. Before 1991, responsibility for financing and managing services in health authorities was integrated. These reforms created the conditions for providers to compete with each other for resources from purchasers (Ham, 1997). Instead of being funded to provide services in their hospitals, health authorities were allocated resources to buy services from Trusts for people who lived in their area. GPs were also given the power to become fundholders to purchase a limited range of services for their patients.

The internal market is now widely perceived to have introduced a degree of unnecessary bureaucracy, fragmentation and competition that acted against the interests of patient care. The Labour government argued in their recent White Paper:

> The introduction of the internal market by the previous government prevented the health service from properly focusing on the needs of patients. It wasted resources administering competition between hospitals. This White

Paper sets out how the internal market will be replaced by a system we have called 'integrated care', based on partnership and driven by performance ...These changes will build on what has worked, but discard what has failed. (Department of Health, 1997).

To this end, the government has decided to retain the separation between purchasers and providers, but to end the fragmentation and competition of the internal market by charging all those concerned with planning and providing health and social services to work to a jointly agreed local Health Improvement Programme.

At what level should services be purchased?

Following the creation of the internal market in the NHS in 1991 and changes in the role of the regions, responsibility for purchasing genetic services was devolved to local Health Authorities. The Genetic Interest Group claimed that the end of the old regional arrangements and the recent trend towards fragmentation threatened to undermine the effectiveness of the service (Genetic Interest Group, 1995). Traditionally, genetic services have dealt with rare disorders which do not affect many people at the district level, although this will change as the genetic components of more common disorders are understood. At present, however, genetics services are not likely to be a high purchasing priority for Health Authorities or for the emerging Primary Care Groups, as purchasers often lack sufficient knowledge about genetic disorders and the services available. Genetic disorders also effect *families* and not all members of a family will live within a single locality.

Providers have also experienced problems with the change in regional arrangements, as regional co-operation is essential for effective evaluation and implementation of genetic services. Regional Genetic Centres have found it harder to negotiate funding for new products and research projects in the NHS after Conservative reforms.

The loss of regional planning is clearly a problem for genetic services, but the Labour government does not propose to bring back Regional Health Authorities. However, the White Paper does foresee a role for NHS Executive Regional Offices in leading and monitoring local action to strengthen partnerships across health and social care, as well as providing the means to commission specialist hospital services (Department of Health, 1997).

The White Paper sets out an increased role for primary care in the commissioning of services. *The New NHS* suggests that a Primary Care Group would typically have a population base of 100,000 (Department of Health, 1997). Regional Genetics Centres and the Genetic Interest Group are concerned that expertise, not to mention resources, could be lost if purchasing decisions for genetic services are devolved to primary care level. Families affected by rare diseases may suffer if funding is increasingly targeted at testing for common, multifactorial diseases, leading to a decrease in the quality of already inadequate services for rare genetic disorders. The Labour government has, however, recognised that the commissioning of some specialist services will be beyond the scope of Primary Care Groups:

> Although most commissioning will pass to Primary Care Groups, Health Authorities will need to work together to commission some specialist services – those organised to serve the population of several Health Authorities, such as bone marrow transplants (Department of Health, 1997).

Genetics as a specialist service?

The Labour government has recently announced in a consultation document that genetics may be one of the services that should be purchased as a specialist service (Department of Health, 1998b). Under these proposals, each of the eight English health regions would have a Regional Specialised Commissioning Group (RSGC) by 1st April 1999. Alan Milburn, Health Minister has said: 'We want to shift the focus onto the quality of care, so that excellence is guaranteed for all patients irrespective of where they live' (Department of Health, 1998b).

This is a welcome development which we support at this stage for the following reasons:

- In genetic services, the unit of interest tends to be family rather than individual

- Contracts between individual purchasers and providers cannot follow families across geographical and Trust boundaries

- The rapid growth and changing nature of the speciality means that genetics will be increasingly relevant to all specialities – it is difficult to isolate genetics into one budget

- Genetics currently affects rare diseases which require a certain level of knowledge and experience not possible at HA or PCG level (although this may change in the future)

- Some genetics services can be prohibitively expensive to a single Health Authority or Primary Care Group (Department of Health, 1995)

At present, genetic services are mainly concerned with rare diseases; the necessary skills base is weak, and it would seem highly inappropriate to allow such services to be purchased at the primary care level at this stage of the development of both the science and the new NHS. However, if, as predicted, genetics increasingly becomes important to all medical specialities and relevant to more common diseases, then it may be appropriate to involve some Primary Care Group Trusts more in the purchasing and provision of genetic services (see chapter 4).

To this end, we must remember that there has been no national review of the different methods being used to purchase genetics services. This would certainly be the first step towards defining more effective models of purchasing in future. It would also make it possible to keep under review the effects of commissioning genetics as a specialist service, and to consider when (if ever) it might be appropriate to allow genetic services to be commissioned at a primary level.

Summary of issues and recommendations

Consensus and coherence on the aims

We cannot really decide how we want genetic services to develop in the NHS until we have decided what we want from genetic services, and equally, what we do not want. At the moment, opinions seem to differ amongst clinical geneticist and public health doctors. It is essential that we have an open and informed debate so that we can all (public and professionals) contribute our view. We therefore recommend:

- An explicit and inclusive debate is needed about the aims of genetic services. Do we support a human rights, clinical or utilitarian approach?

- The Human Genetics Advisory Committee should facilitate an informed public and professional debate on these issues

- Greater emphasis on positively welcoming children and adults affected by genetic conditions into our society should be encouraged, in order to facilitate informed choices

Once we are clear about the aims of genetic services in general, this will aid us in our judgements of the appropriateness of individual genetic tests and screening programmes in particular. We need to establish a consensus not just on the aims of genetic services, but also on the criteria by which we measure success. This requires a multi-disciplinary approach, involving clinical geneticists, users, public health doctors, carers, GPs and the general public:

- Until the above debate happens, a reduction in morbidity and mortality should not be used to measure genetic services, although they may sometimes be a consequence of informed choice

- Purchasers should have an obligation to be open about their decision making processes and criteria

- We need mechanisms for ensuring that geneticists and public health specialists have the opportunity to share their relevant knowledge and experience at both a local and national level and to contribute to the work of the National Institute for Clinical Excellence.

Ensuring that genetic services are purchased at the appropriate level

The abolition of the internal market and the recognition of the importance of co-operation and collaboration are welcome developments. The new Labour government is clearly committed to ending division and fragmentation, and ensuring greater equity of access to quality services for all. However, in order to ensure that this aim is achieved in practice, we recommend:

- Genetics should be purchased as a specialist service and commissioned accordingly *at this stage*

- We need to monitor purchasing arrangements for genetic services and keep under review as the new genetics develops

- Future changes in the pattern of health service purchasing must allow for the family based nature of clinical genetics, for the frequent crossing of geographical boundaries and for the need to incorporate new developments.

4. Who should provide which genetic services?

During the next decade we are likely to witness important developments in the science of genetics. What was a service for rare single gene disorders will increasingly become relevant to other common diseases. These anticipated developments will change traditional boundaries and divisions between professionals and institutions, and increase the pressure for new structures for delivering and gaining access to genetic services.

What kind of genetic services should be provided by whom and at what level? How many staff will be needed and with what skills? How can we facilitate a co-ordinated and integrated approach to service delivery? How can we share and level up existing best practice? How can we ensure that future policy development is driven by an assessment of competence and concern for standards, rather than traditional structures or professional boundaries?

Below we briefly set out how genetic services are currently organised in the UK and highlight the issues and problems which anticipated developments may raise and which policy makers will need to address in order to ensure the effective, equitable and efficient provision of genetic services in the future. Where appropriate we propose practical policies, but are conscious that, given the pace of anticipated change, we must avoid being too rigid or prescriptive about future strategies. In this chapter we shall concentrate on the delivery of genetic services by the public sector. The commercial provision of genetic services, an increasingly important issue, is discussed in detail in Chapter 5.

Current organisation of genetic services

Clinical genetic services are currently organised on a regional basis with populations ranging from two million to five million. Consultant Clinical Geneticists (CCG) are employed to head the team in the Regional Genetics Centre. The role of the CCG has evolved over the past 20 years, and consists of a number of different principal activities:

- Provide genetic diagnoses

- Provide genetic counselling

- Maintain genetic registers

- Provide education

- Hold joint clinics

- Undertake research

- Maintain links with genetics laboratories

- Interface with public health medicine and primary care (REF)

Genetics is essentially a family based service and as families are rarely confined to a single health authority, such boundaries are widely believed to be inappropriate. A regional service allows for an efficient centralised system of records, and for the outcome of screening, counselling and investigations to be monitored. There appears to be a professional and user consensus that comprehensive genetic services should continue to be organised on a regional basis. The Advisory Committee on Genetic Testing noted that the current organisation of genetic services in the UK will provide an important safeguard against the inappropriate or excessive use of genetic tests (ACGT, 1998). However, the future role of Clinical Geneticists is expected to change over the next decade.

Changing role of Clinical Geneticists

The conventional model of service delivery has developed around the diagnosis and treatment of rare and single gene disorders, and may not be appropriate for multifactorial disorders with low penetrance genes. The Department of Health predicted that the huge increase in the number of genetic tests available, and their increasing relevance to the health of many individuals will mean that in the future genetic services are more likely to be offered outside the regional centres, for example in primary care, antenatal clinics and general medical outpatient departments.

Such changes in the role of clinical geneticists may be necessary and welcome. There are only 200 Clinical Geneticists and genetic co-workers in the country, compared with 33,000 GPs, to serve a population of 57 million. Clinical Geneticists may be unable to provide sufficient counselling, or may not be close enough to families to know the nuances of their relationships which can be important in providing a successful service.

It is generally anticipated that Regional Genetics Centres could and should continue to provide services for the rare, single gene disorders but that primary care will become increasingly involved in the provision of genetic services for some common disorders. Clinical geneticists may increasingly fulfill an educational role; for example, helping the primary care groups to deal with the more straightforward cases and setting referral criteria so that they can become involved when appropriate.

However, the predicted shift of genetic services from regional to primary care is far from unproblematic. Some Clinical Geneticists claim that GPs lack the time, interest, skills, and knowledge to provide a sufficiently high standard of genetic services. There are fears that expertise, not to mention resources, could be lost if decisions are devolved to primary level. Families suffering from rare diseases have also expressed concern that funding will increasingly be targeted at common, multifactorial diseases, leading to a decrease in the quality of the already inadequate services for rare genetic disorders. Below we explore the challenges and issues which will need to be addressed if primary care workers are to play an effective and appropriate role in the future provision of genetic services.

The potential role of primary care

In *The New NHS: Modern – Dependable* the government signalled quite clearly the central role of primary care in delivering and purchasing health care services in the future. The Primary Care Groups outlined in the White Paper will extend the role of primary and community healthcare, and bring together GPs and community nurses in each area to work to improve the health of local people (Department of Health, 1997).

Possible roles for GPs in the provision of genetic services

Long before the White Paper was published, it was widely anticipated that General Practitioners would play a central role as both providers and gatekeepers to a range of community genetic services:

> The 32,000 general practitioners in Britain are responsible for primary and continuing care and outnumber all other medical groups. They are therefore uniquely well placed to

deal with families with genetic disorders as well as individual patients. (Harris, 1991).

So what role might primary care actually play? In their second report to the NHS Central Research and Development Committee, the DoH recommended that the role of primary care could include the following responsibilities:

- to assess the subject's preconceived ideas about the aetiology of disease

- discuss perceptions of risk

- construct a family pedigree (take a family history)

- assess the risk of developing disease from the pedigree or empirical risk tables

- help to guide families to appropriate surveillance programmes

- identify families eligible for genetic testing and refer to specialist testing centre

- identify and refer individuals who could benefit from psychological counselling (Department of Health, 1995).

The above paints a role for GPs as information guides and gatekeepers to services. According to this model, GPs will need to be trained to take a good family history and recognise who will benefit from a referral to others (such as Genetic Nurse Specialist), but should not provide services themselves, unless they have a particular interest in that field.

Others anticipate a more ambitious role for primary care, suggesting that GPs could be involved in the provision of two types of screening programmes for genetic disorders in the future. These would include screening for the early onset single gene disorders, which have been available, albeit somewhat inadequately, for some time, such as sickle cell, Thalassaemia and Tay-Sachs; and screening for susceptibility to the common diseases of middle life, such as heart disease, cancer and diabetes, although these latter services are not yet commonly available. This model is perceived by some to be desirable for the following reasons:

When prospective carrier screening is possible, a primary health care based policy of common information, screening and counselling provides by far the best medical service to the groups at risk and also leads to the greatest short- and long-term savings (Royal College of Physicians, 1989).

Pilot Studies for cystic fibrosis carrier testing have indicated that GPs can successfully integrate genetic counselling and carrier screening into the first Antenatal booking appointment. (Harris et al, 1993).These pilot programmes could become the basis for future development of services. This model of GPs as providers has been supported by the Royal College of Physicians, who stated:

GPs and others in Primary Care are in a particularly favourable position to recognise genetic problems and to utilise new developments in genetics. They, like Consultant Clinical Geneticists, are commonly concerned with the family as a unit, while their existing involvement with community based preventive measures, such as immunisations and cervical cancer screening, makes the primary care setting a logical one for genetic screening programmes such as cystic fibrosis carrier screening (Royal College of Physicians, 1989).

Issues raised by genetics in primary care

But are GPs willing to deliver this ambitious agenda? In the same report, the Royal College of Physicians admitted:

The need for appropriate training in genetic issues of those in primary care, and for links between specialists and primary care practitioners is increasingly recognised and represents a major challenge. (Royal College of Physicians, 1989)

Below we identify what some of these challenges might be, before proposing how they might be met and by whom.

Education and training

One of the prime objectives must be to ensure that GPs are appropriately trained. Even if we accept the model of primary care as a gatekeeper and guide to genetic services, there is still a need to educate doctors so that appropriate referral patterns can develop. Alistair Kent, Director of the Genetic Interest Group has pointed out that patients do not go to the doctor saying 'I think I have a genetic disorder'. As he put it, it is a matter of getting a light to come on the GP's head saying, 'I wonder if this is genetic?' so that they can refer to them accordingly.

> Unless you have heightened awareness at the level of Primary Care, who are the gatekeepers, then you can have the most wonderful structures in the world, but you won't get people through it (GIG, 1995a).

Information Technology could play an important role in helping GPs to identify those at risk of inherited disorders, and GIG have suggested piloting a 'decision tree' which would facilitate this process (GIG, 1995a). Decision Support Systems are already being designed to assist the clinical profession in making decisions (Fox, 1998).

The genuine lack of knowledge and understanding about genetics at the primary care level must be recognised. There is evidence that many GPs tend to find interpreting probabilistic information difficult, have a varying tolerance of uncertainty and lack in confidence in imparting uncertain information (Geller & Holzman, 1991). GPs may therefore find counselling families about possible interventions to ameliorate the environmental causes of disease problematic. Indeed, are they willing and able to deal with the complexities of probability, risk and uncertainty? Many GPs do not yet feel a need to prepare for the kind of practice in which predispostional genetic testing for susceptibility to common disorders may become as routine as assessing biological or behavioural risk factors is now (Kinmouth et al, 1998).

Increasing training in genetics and communication skills, will be essential. Basic genetic information and counselling techniques could be included in the curricula for doctors, nurses and other health and social care workers. Research has been undertaken into how genetic information is given by professionals with no direct training in genetics. A recent national audit has been carried out into genetic counselling by non-geneticists (Harris et al, forthcoming). The audit found that poor quality hospital records often lack clear evidence that choices have been made by patients, and that non-geneticists tend to concentrate on the management of the disease to the extent of overlooking the need for counselling. The authors conclude that improvements in clinical practice are necessary, and improved documentation should be encouraged using nationally agreed proformas. They also call for improvements in undergraduate medical and nursing education to cover the basics of genetic management and prevention of disease.

It is worth noting that improved communication and counselling to enable patients to make informed choices should be a feature of all medical consultations, not just those concerned with genetics, and that efforts should be made to level up best practice across all health care services. However, such developments will have serious implications for the most important resource in primary care: time.

Do GPs have the time?

GPs often complain that they are already overloaded with information and bureaucracy, and may therefore be reluctant or unable to take on the extra workload that development in genetics will generate. GPs will need time to explain the many choices which genetic knowledge may present, particularly if they are to relieve patient anxiety. Pilot screening programmes for early onset single gene disorders such as cystic fibrosis have indicated that counselling and obtaining a mouthwash sample add about ten minutes to the first Antenatal or about six hours per annum for an average of 36 pregnancies per general practitioner (Harris et al, 1993)

It may be necessary to guarantee minimum consultation times for certain categories of patients or consultations, and support these accordingly. The use of appropriately trained staff will help to deal with some of the extra work load. For example there may be a role for 'genetic associates' who would operate from a base in the regional genetics centre but be responsible for the organisation of genetic services in primary care. However, increasing the size of primary care teams can also cause problems in terms of co-ordination and communication.

Can GPs work collaboratively?

Whichever model of service provision is favoured, GPs will not be able to go it alone, as the quality of their service will depend upon their working in partnership with others. GPs may find it necessary to devolve some of their tasks so that counsellers, nurse practitioners and perhaps Genetic Nurse Specialists can take on some of the workload. Some have questioned whether GPs can be expected to work co-operatively with other co-workers:

> The autonomous, self-employed status of GPs means that they cannot be relied on working collaboratively for strategic goals. Most of them favour a model of primary health care: one that starts with a diagnosis of illness and ends with a clinical intervention to treat it. There are widespread doubts about their capacity to pursue the public health agenda (Duggan, 1995).

However, whilst the recent White Paper does not affect the independent contractor status of GPs, the emphasis is very much on encouraging them to work collaboratively with other health professionals in order to improve health care services for the wider community.

In the new NHS, Health Authorities are now charged with drawing up a strategy for meeting the needs of their local population in the form of a Health Improvement Programme, developed in partnership with all the local interests and ensuring delivery of the NHS contribution to it. There will be a new statutory duty of partnership placed on local NHS bodies to work together for the common good. The Health Improvement Programmes (HIP) will cover a three year period, and the first HIP programmes are due to be in place by April 1999 (Department of Health, 1997).

Primary Care Groups will also be expected to promote the health of the local population, working in partnership with other agencies to develop primary are by joint working across practices and to integrate primary and community health services by working more closely with social services (Department of Health, 1997). Primary Care Groups will be held to account by health authorities, who will monitor their performance against these duties. Of course, it remains to see how effective this strategy may be in practice, but it seems clear that the role of general practice will gradually evolve into a more collaborative model.

Are GPs willing and able?

Some commentators have warned that primary health care involvement in genetic screening doesn't yet indicate that it would be a good idea to encourage this development at present. They argue that it would be more appropriate to try to improve and level up the genetic services currently provided by GPs, before expanding their role any further. There will clearly be variation in the ability of different primary care teams to deliver good quality genetic services, but this is surely true of all health care services.

For example not all GPs have the facilities to provide regular cervical screening programmes, and their patients are referred elsewhere. However, the larger practices have 'Well Woman' clinics, that provide an excellent service. If some GPs are not capable of providing screening, it does not follow that those who can should not be allowed to do so. It would seem sensible to encourage and support those GPs who are able to provide genetic services to do so, and to concentrate resources on levelling up those who cannot, whilst ensuring that they are aware of appropriate referral protocols. This strategy could form part of the Government's commitment to Clinical Governance.

A far more important question, but one that is rarely asked is, is whether GPs want to be involved in genetic services, and if so to what extent. Many GPs may have very real objections to a further extensions of their already overburdened role. Time and resources are key problems, but there are subtle, but powerful changes associated with genetics that some GPs may wish to resist. Genetics represents a move away from the diagnose and cure model to a predict and prevent model of health care. Do GPs wish to be primarily concerned with giving lifestyle advice? Genetics also requires the doctor not to tell a patient what he or she should do to get better, but to present the options and probabilities so that the patient (or co-producer of health) can make an informed choice. Is this what GPs are trained to do? What are the implication for those who find themselves in a job which they no longer recognise, and for recruiting and training the next generation of GPs?

These cultural changes are to an extent already happening, but the developments in genetics makes them more pertinent. Some have suggested that if GPs prove unwilling to provide genetic services, then a system of incentives may need to be explored, as in immunisation programmes. However, Item of Service payments for genetic services might be thought inappropriate as any element of persuasion (coercion) could be deemed eugenic.

Other NHS professionals and providers

GPs are not capable of delivering genetic services single handedly, and there are not enough Consultant Clinical Geneticists to give them the support they may need. We therefore need to look imaginatively at the contribution which other co-workers could make, such as Genetic Nurse Specialists and Nurse Practitioners.

Genetic Co-workers/Nurses

Clinical genetic co-workers or Genetic Nurse Specialists (GNS) are mostly specialist nursing staff and could provide a focus for future developments. The GNS links the Regional Genetic Centre with the community. Based at the regional or district level, nurse specialists are in a better position to keep up to date with technological developments which is vital if standards of care are to be kept high, whilst remaining accessible enough to provide effective care at the primary level. GNS may play an important role in training primary care teams, although they must be given the time and the money to do so.[1]

For example, the Institute of Medical Genetics in Cardiff uses GNS to provide an interface between the Regional Genetics Centre and families. The larger district hospitals in the region each have one GNS who is responsible to a Clinical Geneticist based at the Institute. The group of GNSs based at Cardiff not only cover Cardiff's population, but each have their own particular disease speciality. However, Wales is better resourced that most other areas of the UK in terms of genetic services.

There are now 108.8 working time equivalent co-workers, a figure exceeding that of Consultant Clinical Genetic posts but falling short of the four per million target given in a Royal College of Physicians report of 1991. In order to attract and retain appropriate staff, the current lack of educational and training programmes for Genetic Nursing Specialists needs to be addressed. It may be necessary to develop a career structure for GNS and other genetic co-workers.

Other Clinical Specialities

Because genetic diseases occur in all body systems and at all ages, genetic advances may increasingly become the common property of all specialists. It has been claimed that there will need to be either a five fold increase in the number of Consultant Clinical Geneticists (which is unrealistic and probably undesirable) or else a programme for ensuring that one in ten of clinicians working in other specialities such as oncology or dermatology are specially trained in the genetics of their disease. This latter approach would ensure that genetic knowledge becomes a part of, rather than apart from every day clinical practice.

Utilising Other Providers – specialist units and laboratories

Instead of thinking about genetics as a distinct and separate service, provided in remote and specialist centres, it is useful to consider how genetics could be grafted onto existing patterns of service provision. For example, in Britain, Family Cancer Clinics are already being established. At present these clinics are essentially research centres, but they could become service providers offering a whole package of care for families. For example, those at risk from breast cancer could go to a FCC and have family history drawn up, followed by genetic testing if a strong family link is indicated. They would be taught self examination and provided with regular screening and advice about the available treatments. FCCs could well provide an innovative model for service development in the future. As recent reports into the treatment of breast cancer have shown, specialist units are the most effective centres for patient care and would therefore continue to provide screening and treatment.

Shifting boundaries

Many of the traditional professional, organisational and cultural assumptions and boundaries in the NHS may no longer be appropriate to the way in which care may need to be delivered in the 21st century. Policy makers and practitioners need to move away from an obsession with means, and concentrate on the functions and ends of health care services. Broadly speaking, the best primary health care can be defined as:

> accessible, holistic, continuing and personalised, and delivered by highly trained generalists supported by community based specialists linked to a wider social care. By implication 'secondary health care' can be understood as services provided by specialists, usually but not necessarily in hospitals to whom referral is essential (Duggan, 1995).

Indeed we may increasingly need to change our ways of thinking about the different levels of service provision – no longer separating the different levels of service provision into primary, secondary and tertiary levels but into to generalist and tertiary levels. Many of the potential problems to the solutions outlined above will require us to think more imaginatively about how GPs can work in partnership with other health care professionals to deliver a good quality genetic service. Greater flexibility of skills and creative deployment will be needed throughout primary health care if we are to meet the complex needs of the patient and the roles of all those involved in health care will have to be constantly reviewed:

> Differentiation between primary and secondary health care must become less distinctive. Political/ organisational changes should be sufficiently flexible to allow and encourage new methods that must be tested for effectiveness, efficiency and economics together with patient satisfaction (Orton & Fry, 1995).

Attention must be paid to the issues of competence and appropriateness, so that the patterns of service deliver are driven by the need to ensure high standards of quality care, not by professional or historical assumptions. It is therefore important that all health care professional and staff recognise their own competence and limitations and share skills where appropriate. Professional entrenchment must be avoided, as must rigid patterns of provision. It may that different types of service provision are appropriate for different types of diseases.

Strategies for the future

The means by which the full potential of Primary Care Groups as the first line providers or gatekeepers of genetic testing have yet to be developed, let alone evaluated. A period of radical experimentation may therefore be not just unavoidable but desirable. It is clear that a broad range of professional skills will be needed if we are to deliver high quality genetic services in the future. The Genetic Interest Group have suggested that, as the scope of the service expands, it becomes more and more important to involve a range of personnel in planning and assessment. They have proposed that each region should have its own community genetics team, comprising:

- family doctor
- clinical geneticist
- genetic nurse specialist
- rep from patient group
- community paediatrician
- public health doctor
- obstetrician
- community midwife
- paediatric pathologist
- health education adviser

This is similar to the proposals put forward by the World Health Organisation for a genetics management team, led by a community genetics co-ordinator, who would usually be a Clinical Geneticist, and by Kinmouth and Reinard, writing in the *BMJ* (Kinmouth et al, 1998).

However, it is questionable whether a Clinical Geneticist, whose primary duty is to individual families, is the most appropriate to lead this team. Both CCG and GPs have no training in public health or population-based strategies.

In order to ensure that the development of genetic services remains consistent with other public health strategies, it may be beneficial to involve the Genetics Community Team in the Health Improvement Programmes proposed by the Labour Government. However there may still be areas of conflict if HIP programmes are agreed at district level, when genetic services need to be planned at regional level.

At the time of writing, there are no figures on how much a Community Genetics Team would cost or indeed save, or how many (if any) regions actually have this and with what effect. This again points to the poor supply of data and analysis on current provision of genetic services, which will make future planning unnecessarily difficult. If the development of genetic services is to be lead by evidence of what works rather than ideology or tradition, then accurate information about the different patterns of genetic services and evaluation data about the relative merits of each model is essential.

Proposals for addressing the need to monitor, evaluate and disseminate best practice in genetics are outlined in Chapter 2, where we argue that due to the high number of committees, commissions and institutes created or proposed in the past two years, it would be unwise to suggest the creation of yet another body. Instead we recommend that the Department of Health should institute a short but multi-disciplinary review to examine how the roles of existing bodies might be extended or strengthened in order to help us achieve these aims.

Summary of issues and recommendations

It is difficult and perhaps undesirable to be too prescriptive about the future development of genetic services in the UK. Current patterns of service a have yet to be fully evaluated, and it is still unclear just how big an impact developments in genetics will have on the NHS over the next decade years. Despite these uncertainties, it is possible to identify the key issues which need to be addressed, and to suggest future policy development and debate.

Changing Role of Regional Genetic Centres

There appears to be a general consensus that the current model of genetic services based at the regional level has developed around the rare and single gene disorders. As genetics continues to impact on multifactorial and common diseases, this model will no longer be sufficient. Future changes, however, should continue to recognise and facilitate the family based nature of genetic services, and the importance of expertise which is maintained at regional level:

- Consultant Clinical Geneticists (CCGs) based at Regional Genetics Centres will probably continue to provide services for the rare and single gene disorders

- CCGs are expected to play a more active role in the education of other NHS professionals and form part of Community Genetic Teams.

The increasing importance of primary care

It is generally anticipated that as genetics impacts on the more common diseases, the scope of primary care involvement will increase. In this chapter we outlined two models of primary care involvement in the provision of genetic services: The GP as gatekeeper and guide to genetic services and the GP as provider of some genetic screening services. It is likely that different approaches will be appropriate for different types of disease, and may even depend on the willingness and ability of individual Primary Care Groups. Regardless of which model develops in primary care, the following issues will need to be addressed in order to ensure the high quality service:

- The lack of knowledge and understanding of genetics in primary care must be recognised and addressed. It may be necessary to improve the current standard of genetic services before expanding the role of GPs

- GPs must be appropriately trained in understanding genetic knowledge and communicating it to others (counselling techniques)

- Information technology could be used to support decisions and disseminate protocols to ensure appropriate referral patterns

- The issue of time needs serious consideration, perhaps through a system of guaranteeing minimum consultation times and/or the use of other primary care workers

- GPs will need to be encourage to work collaboratively with other co-workers; the Health Improvement Programmes may support this

- Primary Care Groups may develop different models of care for different diseases, but they should be evaluated so that we can learn what works

- It is vital that GPs are consulted before developing unrealistic models for the future. Are they willing and able to deliver what is increasingly expected of them?

The role of other NHS professionals and services

If, as expected, genetics becomes a feature of all clinical specialities, developments will impact on all aspects of the health service and those who work in it. GPs will not be able to deliver genetic services by themselves and will require a range of co-workers to enable them to meet the needs of their patients.

- The Genetic Nurse Specialists or co-workers could provide a focus for future developments, linking the Regional Genetic Centres with the community

- Genetic Nurse Specialists (GNS) will need education and training programmes, with a proper career structure in order to ensure that the appropriate staff are attracted and retained

- Community Genetic Teams may provide a useful model for drawing together a range of expertise at the community level

- Consider how to ensure that (approximately) one in ten of those working in other clinical specialities have a good understanding of genetics, and how they can act as a resource for others

- Consider ways in which genetics can build on existing patterns of provision where appropriate, such as Family Cancer Clinics

A National Genetic Service: co-ordination and evaluation

There is a lack of a co-ordinated or coherent approach to genetic services delivery and few data on the impact which these have had on service quality. This important gap in our knowledge will act as an impediment to the future development of genetic services. In Chapter 2 we highlighted the importance of a coherent strategy for the introduction of genetic tests and the need to evaluate different mechanisms of access and delivery of those services, and suggested a review to consider how the role of existing bodies might be extended or strengthened to provide the following functions:

- Monitor and evaluate current patterns and methods of delivering genetic services

- Disseminate best practice, possibly in the form of IT protocols and decision support systems

- Act as an information resource to GPs and Clinicians, providing information on different tests for different diseases, and when it might be appropriate to refer

The importance of competence driven models for the future

Although above we have listed some of the anticipated developments in terms of how they may affect particular professionals, it is important to repeat that future changes should be driven by competence and quality not by organisational structures. The format we have used to summarise the key issues refers to where we are now, so that we might consider where we might want to be in the future. Although it is not clear what shape the future organisation of genetic services might, take the following themes can be identified:

- We are living through a period of organisational change and rapid scientific development.

- These ongoing changes will continually challenge traditional boundaries between professions and institutions.

- It may therefore be more appropriate to think in terms not of primary/secondary care, but generalist/specialist care.

- Future staffing levels and roles need to be driven by competence models, not professional entrenchment.

Endnotes

1   Dr Michael Modell, University College London, is developing a pilot project for the haemoglobinopathies where genetic nurse specialists are being sent into individual practices to train GPs.

5. Genetic tests supplied direct to the public

In the UK, genetic services are currently provided almost exclusively by the NHS. The General Practitioner essentially acts as gatekeeper, and can refer patients to see a Consultant Clinical Geneticist if necessary. Yet what if this gateway to genetic services is kept shut, and the NHS is unable or unwilling to meet predicted demand? Resources are already stretched, and as noted in the previous chapter, GPs have varying degrees of knowledge or interest in the new genetics. Could or should there be a role for the private sector in providing genetic tests in the future? As one commentator has noted:

> Meeting the rising demand for genetic information and advice will require a major reorganisation of genetic services. In the United States, demand has led to the growth of private genetics services that are marketed directly to the public. In the United Kingdom, specialist genetics services are struggling to cope (Kinmonth et al, 1998).

Should Government encourage or allow the commercial sector to meet demand for genetic services, or is there a need to regulate non-NHS activity in this area? If so, why? How do genetic tests differ from other diagnostic services? Will regulation protect the public or stifle scientific progress? What impact would a private market in genetic tests have on the NHS? It is difficult, if not impossible, to develop policy in such a fast moving area. As an editorial in *Nature* magazine noted, 'the debate [about genetic testing] becomes even more complex when commercial factors come into play' (*Nature*, 1996). Our aim in this chapter is therefore not to be too prescriptive, but to identify the issues which will need to be addressed if, as predicted, a commercial market develops for the provision of genetic tests in the UK.

First we briefly outline the existing range and use of genetic tests supplied directly to the public, before discussing why it might be necessary and appropriate to regulate this growing field of activity. Secondly, we outline and assess the current regulation and guidelines which govern the commercial provision of genetic tests, before setting out options for managing the provision of genetic tests supplied direct to the public in the future.

Current commercial provision of genetic tests

In Chapter 1 we outlined the different types of genetic tests which were (or will be) available for different types of diseases. Here we consider which type of genetic tests could or should be provided by the commercial sector direct to the public, under what (if any) circumstances.

Box 5.1

Direct to the public (UK)

London-based University Diagnostics have adapted a genetic test for use in the home, which identifies cystic fibrosis carriers. This carrier test is designed to assess a couple's chance of having a child with cystic fibrosis. The test costs £95 per couple, and accurately detects common forms of genetic changes that can cause cystic fibrosis. Postal testing for Down's syndrome is also available. The Select Committee on Science and Technology (HCSCST, 1995), which examined the question of commercial provision of genetic tests claimed 'we know of no postal diagnostic services for late onset diseases ... such as breast cancer and Huntington's ...Were such services to be introduced without adequate counselling, the effects could be devastating'.

Direct to public (USA)

Companies in the USA have begun to market the first broad based genetic tests for late onset diseases. Myriad Genetics, of Salt lake City, Utah and IVF offer tests for the breast cancer genes *BRCA1* and *BRCA2*. Full sequence testing for these mutations are available from Myriad for $2,400. They have also recently advertised for Jewish women to be tested for the *185delAG* deletion. This mutation is found in one per cent of women of Eastern European Jewish ancestry, and has been associated with breast cancer (*Nature*, 1996).

Key concerns

Below we outline some commonly expressed concerns about genetic tests supplied direct to the public, before considering the extent to which a market for such tests may develop in the UK, and what (if any) response is required from policy makers.

Inflate inappropriate demand

As more genetic tests become available, there are concerns that testing might be offered for genes which have weak or poorly understood associations with common diseases. As the Select Committee on Science and Technology warned: 'There is a very real danger that unscrupulous companies may prey on the public's fear of disease and genetic disorders and offer inappropriate tests, without adequate counselling and even without the lab facilities necessary to ensure that they are conducted accurately'(HCSCST, 1995). The NHS may also find itself under increased pressure to provide tests of dubious benefit as the public becomes increasingly aware of the availability of such tests in the commercial sector.

Fuel anxiety

Companies who market genetic tests may raise unnecessary alarm and fuel anxiety. Neil Holtzman, chair of a joint NIH Department of Energy Task Force on Genetic Testing, has criticised companies for advertising genetic tests for breast cancer, claiming that Myriad Genetics, of Salt Lake City, Utah and IVF overstate the risk of breast cancer among women with the *BRCA1* and *BRCA2* mutations by using data from the most dramatically affected families in order to increase demand for their services (*Nature*, 1996).

NHS may be left to pick up the pieces

The NHS could be left to pick up the burden and cost of those who have first accessed the private sector. Patients may seek explanations from their GP who will in turn refer them for counselling at a Regional Genetic Counselling Centre, who may repeat the test if they are unsure of the quality and competence of the original provider, adding to the strain on resources. If commercial genetic tests for breast cancer were provided, this could have a direct impact on the utilisation of a wide range of NHS facilities which may be requested for diagnosis, prevention and treatment, for the individual and their family members (Harper, 1997d).

Cream off cheap services

Commercial companies may choose to ignore all the evidence that points to the need for (costly) counselling, and instead develop a purely laboratory (and therefore cheaper) approach to testing (Harper, 1997d). NHS research laboratories have also expressed concerns that commercial companies could cream off the 'easy' and marketable tests, leaving the NHS to develop the costly tests for 'orphan' diseases.

Erode the principle of equity

For families at risk of inherited disease, speedy access to comprehensive integrated genetic services is an important factor in giving reproductive confidence and choice. Commercial testing, irrespective of its quality, is potentially discriminating in that it is only available to those who can afford it. Individuals who can afford a commercial test which they will not have to share with their GP may also be able to avoid discrimination by insurance companies and employers (see Chapter 6).

Confidentiality

There are fears (although no evidence) that a commercial company would not be covered by the same professional codes as the NHS, and that genetic information could be shared with or sold to other organisations without the patient's consent. Others have questioned whether commercial companies might be tempted to test a DNA sample taken for one purpose and test it for other diseases, again without the patients' consent or knowledge.

Commercial interest vs public interest

As an editorial in *Nature* noted, when commercial companies provide tests for genetic disorders, '... there is always a concern that the promise of fat dividends for shareholders is a major driving force behind any company's involvement in the health field' (*Nature*, 1996). Since commercial success will equate with numbers of people tested, will there be pressure for testing to be maximised, in terms of the way that information is given? This could undermine the concept of non-directive counselling, which is central to genetic services (Harper, 1997d).

Quality in public and private sectors

There are concerns that the commercial imperative will have a detrimental effect on quality. Costs may be cut in order to maximise profit, with patients suffering as a result. This is a legitimate concern, but it is worth noting that the NHS also has to operate within increasingly tight budgets, and there are often strong incentives within the system to cut, avoid or shift costs.

One witness to the Science and Technology Committee claimed that a system of avoiding costs had developed, with some health authorities taking mouth wash samples for cystic fibrosis, and only informing and providing counselling to couples where both are carriers. This means that for several thousand tests a health authority only has to provide counselling for 8-10 couples, instead of the one in every 25 that carries the mutation (HCSCST, 1995). This may result in a false and dangerous sense of security when partners are changed.

Commercial companies may have strong incentives to make a profit, but a public sector under financial strain also has an incentive to cut or avoid costs. Both can result in compromising patient care and a dilution of quality. Therefore, any form of regulation or guidelines should apply to both public and private sectors, and act as a driver for quality.

The future role of commerical genetic tests

Before considering how (if at all) public policy might address the concerns outlined above, we must first of all address two key questions. First, what is the size of the problem which we need to address? To what extent is over-the-counter genetic testing likely to be a feature of future service provision? Secondly, what is the *nature* of the problem which we need to address? How, if at all do genetic tests differ from other medical tests offered over-the-counter, and does this warrant a particular policy response?

What will be the size of the OTC market?

Professor Peter Harper considered the concerns raised by the prospect of private sector involvement in genetic testing, and concluded that 'I can see neither need for, nor benefit from over-the-counter testing', optimistically predicting that it will remain a negligible element in our provision of genetic services for genetic diseases in the future (Harper, 1997d).

However, an alternative prediction was made by Professor Morton Warner, who painted the following scenario:

> Currently mail order testing for cystic fibrosis carrier status exists in the UK; and a plethora of diagnostic kits for a wide variety of common genetic disorders is already being promised. It is not too far-fetched to envisage the high street chemist of the future, alongside their photo-development, cholesterol testing, and mother and baby care, providing a complete genetic testing and counselling service (Welsh Institute for Health and Social Care, 1998).

As we cannot predict the future, it is impossible to say which scenario will prevail. However, one thing is clear about the society which we live in: a market will always develop where there is public demand for a particular service. Public demand is therefore likely to be a key factor in the future development (or not) of over-the-counter genetic tests.

Is there public demand for commercial tests?

Genetic tests for susceptibility genes such as *BRCA1* and *BRCA2* are already being marketed and sold direct to the public in the US, but what evidence is there that the public would wish to access such services in the UK? Little research currently exists in this area, but a small-scale survey of 34 members of the patient groups' umbrella organsiation The Genetic Interest Group, found that 70 per cent would consider it reasonable to use commercial facilities for testing asymptomatic children, even for tests of low accuracy (Genetic Interest Group, 1997a).

As one commentator has observed: 'The sense within this small population seemed to be that individuals should have control and responsibility for their own decisions (and decisions affecting their children) in this area. If the NHS did not provide access to genetic testing on an equitable basis, then the sentiment was that commercial testing provided an alternative' (Wilke, 1997).

The University of Glamorgan recently carried out research into informed public opinion about the provision of genetic services, when it commissioned a citizens' jury at the end of 1997. Amongst other recommendations, the jury concluded that:

> Individuals should remain free to use private genetic testing services offered within current regulation ...The private provision of healthcare services has always existed alongside the NHS and often private initiatives that widen public access to health care services are to be welcomed ...Maintaining as much freedom of choice as possible in genetic testing is crucial, regardless of whether this is the freedom to avail of a mail order genetic test or to go to a private genetic counsellor (Welsh Institute for Health and Social Care, 1998).

It would appear that the public support a role for the private sector in the provision of genetic tests. These two (albeit small) pieces of research are perhaps indicative of a deeper shift occurring in our society, where there is an increasing willingness amongst the public to self medicate for certain diseases. Patients are less likely to view their GP as the only source of advice or the only point of access to health care. Over the past few years several medicines have moved from Prescription Only Medicine (POM), to Pharmacist (P) and sometimes to the General Sales List (GSL). Ibuprofen is one example of this (PAGB 1997). The recent banning of Viagra on the NHS has prompted private clinics to offer prescriptions to meet demand (*The Guardian*, 1998).

The development of commercial genetic tests must be seen within the context of a wider shift towards over-the-counter medicines in general. We are clearly moving away from the paternalistic model of health care, with the patient as a passive follower of advice, towards an emerging model where the patient is an active participant in maintaining their own health care. These developments lead us to suspect that there is a potential market for genetic tests offered direct to the public.

Box 5.2 – Growth in OTC medicines

Boots has reported a great increase in demand for home-testing products, especially in the past 12 months. The home pregnancy-test market alone is growing by about 12 per cent a year. Pregnancy tests cost around £9 and are 99 per cent effective. Blood pressure tests are now available from chemists, with blood pressure monitors ranging from £70–£160. Tests for diabetes are also available from chemists, with urine analysis available for just £4.23 (although an item in the *BMJ* suggested the tests are often unreliable, inappropriate and could increase anxiety). Kits such as the Home Cholesterol Test (£7.99) measures fat concentration from a drop of blood on the finger. However, cholesterol levels can vary greatly from day to day. Home Access Health Corporation in America has also developed an HIV test, set to come to the UK soon (*Evening Standard*, 1997).

Should we welcome this shift uncritically, and support the development of over-the-counter genetic tests in the name of patient empowerment, or are there important differences between genetic tests and other OTC medicines that justify professional or political intervention?

Are genetic tests different from other medical tests?

Given that there has been such a growth in over-the-counter diagnostic medicines in general, why are we concerned about the possibility of over-the-counter genetic tests in particular? Is there something distinct about genetic information which requires a different response from policy makers?

Janet Haskell, President of Myriad Genetic Laboratories has argued 'there's really no difference between a blood cholesterol test and a genetic test. No-one has given me a good reason why this type of test would require FDA oversight, whereas others do not' (Nature, 1997a). Below we set out some of the most commonly cited reasons why genetic tests may differ from other medical tests, before discussing just how appropriate these distinctions are.[1]

Information is uncertain and may offer dilemmas

A pregnancy kit offers a clear diagnosis; a woman is either pregnant or not. A genetic diagnosis may not be so clear cut, and incomplete knowledge may be more confusing than ignorance, presenting people with dilemmas rather than choices. This means that the consultation before and after a genetic test may be different to that needed in other forms of treatment. People tested, and indeed, sometimes their relatives, may need to understand what the results means for them before the test is performed.

Predictive power

The ACGT note that the distinctive feature of some genetic tests is their power to predict the potential future health of the individual.

> This possibility to foretell the future with scientific confidence is a totally new feature in medical tests, and has particular significance in relation to employment and insurance (ACGT, 1998)

Information changes

A great deal is still unknown about the relationship between genetics and disease and there is sometimes a need to return to families with updated information regarding their diagnosis or treatment. It is useful for a GP to know of the diagnosis, so that when more information or treatment becomes available, the affected person/s can be informed and ensure continuity of care.

The unit of confidentiality

Confidentiality is important in all areas of medicine, but genetic information poses more complex challenges. Human genetic tests can differ from most other clinical tests which only involve a single individual, because they may also reveal important information about relatives and can have a great impact upon families. Therefore the very unit of confidentiality may not be the individual, but the family (GIG, 1998).

The cost of the service is time related

It takes a great deal of time to give genetic information in pre and post counselling. Commercial companies and hard pressed NHS bodies may be tempted to cut costs in this labour intensive area.

The clinic and laboratory are interdependent

New genes and techniques are constantly being added to the service. Commercial testing in laboratories which do not share their results with the NHS may restrict progress and knowledge.

Discussion

In an interesting and challenging paper, Dr. Ron Zimmern offers a conceptual exploration of genetic testing, and questions whether genetic information can be adequately defined and categorised in any meaningful way (Zimmern, 1998b). Dr. Zimmern argues that the ethical and social implications outlined above arise not from the nature and technology of the test procedure, but from the nature of the disorder itself. There is, he claims, no difference between a diagnosis being made through the use of DNA technology compared to a diagnosis which comes about as a result of a biochemical or a radiological test. The important distinction, he argues, is not between DNA testing and other forms of diagnosis, but in the different types of diseases, namely Mendelian as opposed to other disorders with a predictive value of genetic risk.

Whilst not agreeing with all of Dr. Zimmern's conclusions, we think he raises some powerful points which require further consideration and debate. Much of this is technical, and cannot be covered in this chapter. However, these issues are very relevant to the question of insurance, and are discussed further in Chapter 6.

We began this section by asking 'are genetic tests different from other type of medical tests?' It is perhaps inappropriate to give a straight yes or no to this question. Some types of genetic tests for certain types of disorders are likely to be significantly different – others less so. It is helpful to return to the distinction made in Chapter 1 between diagnostic and predictive testing. Genetic tests that give a diagnosis of a current condition in adults may raise no new issues for policy makers, and it is questionable whether they need additional regulation other than that which is already provided for other over-the-counter diagnostic medicines (OTC). However, predictive testing (both presymptomatic and predispositional) would appear to raise particular issues (as outlined above) that require our particular attention. It may be that other forms of non-genetic predictive tests (such as cholesterol testing) also needed to be considered in this context.

Current regulatory framework

After considering the issues raised by the commercial provision of genetic tests, The Select Committee on Science and Technology recommended 'as a matter of urgency that there should be a body able to regulate companies offering genetic screening through a process of protocol review and licensing' (HCSCST, 1995).

The Government responded by establishing The Advisory Committee on Genetic Testing in July 1996. (See p. 33 for terms of reference) They have since published a Code of Practice for genetic testing offered commercially to the public. Their aim is to:

> ensure that such services are delivered with the best interests
> of those tested in mind and that appropriate information and
> genetic consultation area available (Advisory Committe on
> Genetic Testing, 1998a)

The ACGT concluded that the role for commercial companies should be limited to those tests which determine carrier status for inherited recessive disorders where such status carries no significant direct health implications for the carrier individual (for example cystic fibrosis). This is because the ACGT believes that the provision of such tests poses fewer difficulties than provision of testing for inherited dominant and X-linked disorders, for adult onset genetic disorders, or for the genetic components of mulitactorial or acquired diseases. In these latter cases, ACGT believes proposals for genetic tests supplied direct to the public will be limited for the following reasons:

● Many test results are too complex to be incorporated into a mail-order over-the-counter test procedures

Box 5.3 – ACGT guidelines on commercial testing

1. Testing laboratories, equipment and reagents

All equipment and reagents for testing should be manufactured and maintained to an appropriate level and provide assured levels of accuracy and reliability. All laboratories offering genetic testing services should be appropriately staffed and equipped, and should participate in an accreditation scheme, join an appropriate external quality assurance scheme and perform adequate internal quality control.

2. Confidentiality and storage of samples and records

Suppliers should keep customer data confidential. Testers should not pass on, or resell, any samples or other customer information to third parties, except for the General Practitioner, but only then following specific written approval of the customer.

3. Tests that may be supplied

Genetic testing offered commercially direct to the public should be restricted to those test which determine carrier status for inherited recessive disorders in which carrier status carries no significant direct health implications for the carrier individual.

4. Who may be supplied tests

Genetic testing services supplied direct to the public should not be supplied to those under the age of 16, or to those unable to make a competent decision regarding testing.

5. Customer information

Suppliers should provide appropriate information to customers giving details of the tested condition, to ensure that the customer understands the nature of the testing, its scope and limitations, and the accuracy, significance and use of a result, before the test is performed.

6. Genetic consultation

Suppliers should provide opportunities for appropriate pre-and post-test consultation for which there should be no additional charge.

7. Involvement of general medical practitioners

Suppliers should supply a copy of test results, with the customer's written consent, to general medical practitioners for inclusion in the customer's health record.

- Prediction of a high chance of a serious health outcome will still be accompanied by uncertainty about when, if the disease will strike and with what severity.

Comment and discussion

Companies proposing to offer any human genetic testing service directly to the public are expected to comply with the Code of Practice and Guidance and present their proposals to the ACGT for comment. This, it is hoped, will 'create a more flexible responsive framework than would be available to statutory schemes', although the status of the code will be kept under review. Whilst many people have welcomed the fact that the ACGT has addressed these issues, some have expressed concern that the Code of Practice is only advisory, rather than statutory.

The Code of Practice – advisory or statutory?

The ACGT does not have the power to ensure adherence to its recommendations. There is technically nothing to stop unscrupulous providers entering the market place, undercutting those who seek to apply a quality service, and driving down standards through commercial pressures. The history of self regulation and toothless watchdogs in the UK does not immediately inspire confidence in this approach. Up to 1.5 million people are thought to have been sold unsuitable pensions in the late 1980s and early 1990s. Mis-selling occurred on a massive scale before regulators acted (*The Observer*, 1997b).

However, others have pointed to the need to avoid the rigidity associated with regulation, and maintain flexibility in this fast moving area of science. It is not just industry which is wary of legislation. Several clinical specialists have warned that regulation may be inappropriate in a medical context, and restrict progress. Yet these are arguments against rigidity, and do not amount to an argument against regulation *per se*. Tom Wilke has argued that:

> When it comes to prescriptive, legally-backed regulation, British constitutional practice has developed a model which combines a high degree of flexibility with continuing Parliamentary oversight. This option was followed for the

Human Fertilisation and Embryology Authority and the Health and Safety Commission ... regulations can be made (and unmade) quickly and without the need for primary legislation. The two organisations also have the power to issue licences specifying to those they regulate what can and cannot be done (Wilke, 1997).

These arguments are convincing. However, it may be unwise to regulate before we know exactly where we are going wrong. It is perhaps appropriate for the ACGT to start off as non-statutory body and work out exactly what needs to be statutory and why before doing so. If there were to be a massive increase in the availability of over-the-counter genetic testing with suppliers not putting their proposals to ACGT, then there would be an urgent need to review procedures and to impose some statutory codes. The HFEA started out as a non-statutory body, so there is a useful precedent for this approach.

At this stage it would therefore appear appropriate to recommend:

- A review of adherence to ACGT Code of Practice

- If significant or emerging divergence from the code, Government should explore flexible forms of regulatory bodies such as HFEA and HSC

What should the ACGT regulate?

Assuming that the ACGT follows the model of the HFEA and evolves into a statutory body, what then should it regulate? Any definitive answer must depend upon the outcome of the review of the code. However, at this stage, there would appear to be two logical areas which could require regulation in the future:

- What tests are provided to whom (pre-market approval)

- Who provides those tests and in what circumstances (accreditation)

Pre-market approval

The ACGT currently requests that companies planning to supply genetic tests direct to the public submit their proposals to them for comment. If the ACGT gained statutory powers, it would be possible to require companies to submit proposals to the ACGT for pre-market approval, in effect creating a licensing scheme for genetic tests which does not currently exist. (This is true of both the public and private sector, see Chapter 2). There is a precedent for this in the Gene Therapy Advisory Committee, which although it is not a regulatory body, can demand to see each gene-therapy research proposal.

However, such procedures may be beyond the capacity and resources of the ACGT. It may therefore be more feasible and appropriate for the ACGT to retain responsibility for drawing up any criteria and guidelines, whilst extending the role of the Medicines Controls Agency (MCA) to cover genetic tests. The MCA already has responsibility for licensing products for use, so this would only require an expansion of their role to include genetic testing, (from both public and private bodies) rather than the creation of another a new body. A proposed European Union directive on *in vitro* diagnostic medical devices provides greater assurance of the quality of tests marketed as kits and reagents[2] (Holtzman & Shapiro, 1998).

If we moved towards a system of pre-market approval, there would be quite legitimate concern that this would restrict progress. If any criteria is too rigid or inflexible, then there is a danger that research and innovation would be stifled. Again, this is an argument against bad regulation, not regulation *per se*.

In the US an expert panel recommended an expansion of government regulation of genetic testing (*Nature*, 1997b). One of their central recommendations was that some tests require 'stringent scrutiny' throughout their development and marketing. This flexible policy would allow certain tests to be introduced (thus preventing research and development from being unduly stifled) whilst also ensuring that the public interest is protected[3] (*Nature*, 1997a). The concept of 'stringent scrutiny' (or perhaps pilots, as we would call them in the UK) would appear to be a useful approach, and worth exploring.

Indeed, criteria should perhaps not just be concerned with the test itself, but with appropriateness. It may not be possible or desirable to decide what is appropriate for everybody, but what is appropriate for which kind of people and diseases and tests. This could provide a way of managing the introduction of genetic tests, so that when a test is developed, it is used appropriately, before being extended on the basis of available evidence.

Similar proposals cover OTC drugs, which can range from Prescription only (PO) Pharmacy (P) and General Sales List (GSL). This principle of staging a shift from prescription only to over-the-counter for carefully defined medicines offers a useful precedent which could be usefully explored. If the ACST develops into a statutory body, we suggest that

• Public and private sector should be required to submit proposals to ACGT or MCA for pre-market approval

• Continue to prohibit predictive testing, but

• Explore ways of managing interface, either through concept of 'stringent scrutiny' or learning from experience of OTC sector

Accreditation for providers

In the United Kingdom, most clinical laboratories are associated with health authorities and are subject to Department of Health rules. The Clinical Molecular Genetics Society established a quality assurance scheme, now operated by an independent body. The Code of Practice produced by the ACGT also contains guidelines for assuring the quality of commercial providers of genetic tests.

However, it remains unclear whether a laboratory which fails to be accredited will be allowed to supply genetic tests direct to the public or to NHS purchasers. In the UK, there is a woeful absence of regulation or accreditation covering the private sector. In the US, a task force called for the setting up under law a national accreditation programme to ensure genetic testing quality, with third-party payers encouraged to reimburse only accredited labs.

A similar policy could be followed here, with NHS purchasers (at present health authorities, but shortly Primary Care Groups) only allowed to contract for genetic services with accredited providers, whether in the public or private sector. The accreditation scheme could also act as a guide for individuals wishing to obtain OTC tests, much as the register scheme for homeopathy operates.[4] The accreditation scheme would create an incentive to drive up quality in the private sector, if it enabled them to enter into large contracts with the NHS, rather than relying on the OTC market.

Whilst there are numerous accreditation provisions to ensure the quality of testing laboratories, equipment and reagents, the question remains whether we need to develop a broader concept of accreditation and quality. For example, although there is the National Accreditation Body, the Clinical Pathology Accreditation and the Medical Devices Regulations, many of these bodies are concerned with clinical standards and staffing levels. Whilst these issues are important, this still leaves many of the concerns identified above unaddressed. What about the need to provide counselling, to guarantee confidentiality, to maintain public trust and confidence? In order to ensure that these issues are addressed, we recommend that any future review of the accreditation scheme includes a wide range of consumer and user groups.

Conclusion

The British system for regulating human genetics is in its infancy. Policy makers are aware of the need to tread with caution, lest we strangle the new genetics at birth. However, the legitimate desire for caution should not be an excuse for inaction. Failure to anticipate and respond to some of the emerging issues could be just as problematic as premature action. As Francis Collins, director of the National Centre for Human Genome Research at the National Institutes of Health has warned:

> One of my fears is that we will commit so many egregious errors early on that the (American) public will decide that they do not want to have anything to do with this technology. We don't need a genetic thalidomide.

It is in the interests of health professionals, the public and industry to develop a fair regulatory framework in order to ensure that this does not happen. The policy options and issues outlined in this chapter are modest but achievable. Their aim is to ensure that the new genetics continues to develop in a way which is beneficial to the general public, whilst satisfying the needs of those who develop and provide the technologies. Our proposals are an attempt to ensure that future developments of the health service in general and genetic technologies in particular are led not by the *ad hoc* demands of individual consumers and the interests of industry, but by a strategic assessment of public need and a continued commitment to protecting the public interest.

Summary of issues and proposals

Although there is currently a tiny market in the commercial provision of genetic tests, developments in the USA point to the need to anticipate worst case scenarios. Potential public demand for commercial genetic tests must be viewed in the context of a wider cultural shift towards more self medication and patient autonomy.

The issue of whether genetic tests differs from other medical tests is not clear cut – the answer is likely to be different for different tests and diseases. We suggest that predictive genetic tests are different, but welcome further debate. In this chapter we drew attention to some of the real and imagined fears surrounding genetic tests supplied direct to the public. The Code of Practice by the ACGT is a welcome attempt to address these concerns. If the market for commercial provision of genetic tests grows, then we recommend the following options should be explored, in an attempt to build upon the work of the ACGT and other bodies:

Development of the ACGT and Code of Practice

- A review of adherence to the Code of Practice should be carried out to identify what (if anything) needs to be made statutory and why

- We anticipate that the ACGT could evolve into a statutory body

- If so, the Government should explore other examples of flexible regulation, as typified by the HFEA and HSC

What regulatory functions might the ACGT carry out?

- Develop a pre-market approval system for the public and private sector (although the ACGT could develop guidelines which would be enforced by an extended MCA)

- To avoid restricting progress, any pre-market approval should allow for flexibility, possibly through the use of 'stringent scrutiny'

- Ensure that the NHS only purchases from accredited providers

- Broaden the concept of accreditation to include the concerns of users.

It is vital that we ensure that a commercial sector does not develop in response to the failure of the NHS to meet appropriate demand. Such a development would result in inequity of access, and create a two-tier health care system. It is the aim of this publication to ensure that NHS professionals are prepared for the challenges ahead, so that all citizens can have access to genetic services on the basis of need and need alone.

Endnotes

1   These distinguishing characteristics are adapted from Dr Helen Hughes's evidence to the House of Commons Science and Technology Committee (1996), where she pointed out what she saw as the differences between genetic disorders and others are.

2   The Department of Health's Manufacturer Registration Scheme does not apply to in vitro diagnostics (IUDs – in which genetic tests are included) and there is no requirement that IUDs be evaluated by the DoH before they are marketed in the UK. However, there is a voluntary evaluation programme for such devices. The European Commission is working on a Directive to control In Vitro Diagnostic Medical Devices, which seven years on has still yet to be adopted.

3   Their proposals came under fire from academics and industry, who feared that a National Genetics Board could slow down the grants process. Others argued that involving the FDA could deal a blow to small companies, as only large companies with deep pockets could afford to develop tests in such circumstances. Myriad warned that any FDA role would 'stifle innovation and diffusion of genetic testing technologies'. The US Government task force eventually dropped its plans to call for the FDA to extend its regulation of genetic tests, due to the lack of consensus on the panel.

4   This scheme, however, needs to tightened up. Anyone can call themselves a homeopath, but most medical bodies advise patients to seek practitioners registered with the British Register of Complementary Practitioners or members of the Society of Homeopaths.

6. Genetic information: privacy, access and discrimination

The National Health Service does not exist in a social vacuum. The extent to which the public accept, demand or avoid genetic testing or screening services in the future will depend in part upon who will have access to genetic information and how they will use it. Dr Arthur Caplan has argued that, 'If you don't protect privacy, people will stay away from genetic testing in droves' (Linnane, 1996).

This highlights why the question of who has access to genetic data is of particular relevance to health professionals and policy makers. A key concern is not just that these issues will affect future levels of demand, but that insurance or employer-related use of genetic tests could undermine the concept of unpressured consent, which is the cornerstone of genetic testing (Harper, 1997e).

It is therefore essential that those concerned with the future development of genetic services in the NHS begin to engage with the debate currently taking place in wider public policy circles: Who should have access to the results of genetic tests and under what (if any) conditions? What would be the consequences of (non) access? How can public policy balance the competing claims of privacy and access?

Sheila McLean made the following observation in her essay *Mapping the Human Genome – friend or foe*:

> ... the potential of genetic information is to set the individual against the community. Whether or not a particular person wishes access to genetic data, and whatever the reason for that desire, he or she will almost certainly see it as information which should be held, controlled and acted upon (or not) by him or her self. For the employer, insurer or the state, the information only has value if it is accessible to them.. Societies are therefore faced with the inevitability of two things. First, that the volume of genetic information will continue to expand, and second that access will seldom, if ever, be restricted only to the individual (McLean, 1997).

There are three main areas in which genetic information has the potential to cause conflict between the competing claims of privacy and access: the individual and the family, the individual and insurance companies, and the individual and his or her employer. In this chapter, we confine ourselves to a discussion on the issues raised by two key areas of public policy, insurance and employment. The complex issues raised by the family are discussed in detail in Marteau and Richard's *The Troubled Helix* (1996).The purpose of this chapter is to outline the dilemmas which questions of access to genetic data raise, provide a synthesis of current policy developments in this area so far, and recommend ways in which they may be taken forward.

Genetic information and Insurance

In America, the debate about genetics and insurance has focused on health insurance, as there is no national health care system, and citizens must instead rely on private cover. The fact that we have an NHS in the UK means that we should avoid the potential for discrimination in most forms of health care. (This may not be true of long term care, which is discussed below.) The issue of access and discrimination, however, is still relevant in the UK for life insurance, which is necessary in order to buy a home in most cases, and is therefore of great importance to most adults. In order to fully understand the debate about genetic information and insurance, it is necessary to understand the principles of insurance.

Principles of insurance

Insurance offers protection against the effects of something unpleasant happening to us. Insurers are professional risk takers, and it is their job to calculate the probability of different types of risk occurring. It is a knowledge-based industry, which uses information to distribute risk and advantage between certain groups. There are basically two exclusive principles which guide this distributional process: mutuality and solidarity. The distinction between these two principles and practices is often overlooked, yet it is central to understanding this public policy debate.

Solidarity

The best example of a solidarity based insurance system in the UK is the National Health Service. This mode of social insurance covers everybody for a defined range of risks: nobody is excluded because they are deemed to be a poor risk. Insurance based on solidarity is typically compulsory; premiums (or in this case taxes) are set either equally or according to ability to pay and there is no direct relationship between an individual's contribution and the benefit that they may be expected to draw. Risk and advantage is therefore distributed *equally* across the board.

Mutuality

Commercial insurance arrangements are typically based on the principle of mutuality. Here purchase is optional, and a proposal may be refused, or the premium increased if the risk is considered higher than normal (for example in car insurance). Those with similar perceived or estimated risks are assigned to the same 'pool' and charged the same premium for a given level of cover; claimants are paid according to their loss or the sum assured. Risk and advantage is therefore only distributed *within* and between defined groups of people bearing similar degrees of risk (Human Genetics Advisory Commission, 1997).

Life insurance, which is based upon the mutuality principle, depends upon accurate disclosure of information which is material to the risk being insured (for example, age, gender, health status and family history). Insurance contracts that are entered into on this basis are said to reflect the utmost good faith (*uberrima fides*) of both parties (Human Genetics Advisory Commission, 1997).

Genetics is of potential use to the insurance industry, as it may enable predictions to be made about the future health and life span of an applicant. The industry argues that unless it has access to the same information as a policy holder, then they will suffer 'adverse selection'. Those who are against insurers having access to genetic information claim that this would result in genetic discrimination. The merits of these competing fears are briefly discussed below.

Adverse selection

The Association of British Insurers is the most prominent body representing the UK insurance industry. It represents about 440 companies, accounting for over 95 per cent of insurance business. They have stated that unless industry is allowed access to the results of genetic tests, they will suffer from what they call adverse selection:

> In the absence of full and accurate disclosure of information, proper evaluation of risk cannot take place. Insurance companies could be 'selected against' by people who know that they are more at risk and would, therefore, benefit by being able to take out high levels of insurance at a price effectively being subsidised by all policy holders (Association of British Insurers, 1997b).

However, not all insurance companies agree with this analysis. Standard Life has rejected this argument, claiming that family history already tells actuaries all that they need to know to underwrite successfully and that it will be another ten years before genetic testing could have a big impact on risk assessment. Angus MacDonald, an actuary, also concluded that the effects on the life insurance industry would be minimal, and that any damage would be related to large size policies (MacDonald, 1997).

The ABI have accepted that if the industry does not have access to genetic tests, then nothing much will happen in the short term. However, they are concerned that if and when genetic testing becomes more common, industry will suffer if this information is not available to insurers. Indeed, Peter Robertson told the *Independent* he could not guarantee that his company's policy would hold in the future. 'Having talked to a number of geneticists, they say we would be foolish to ignore genetic tests forever, because they may prove to be exceptionally useful'.

However, The Human Genetics Advisory Commission considered the issue of adverse selection in its report on the implications of genetic testing for insurance, and appeared unconvinced by the industry's arguments. It concluded that 'the life insurance industry could currently withstand limited adverse selection that might occur as a result of non-disclosure of genetic tests for life insurance' (HGAC, 1997).

Discrimination

Many witnesses who gave evidence to the House of Commons Select Committee which looked at the issue of genetics expressed concern that the disclosure of genetic information could lead to genetic discrimination, particularly in relation to insurance and employment. As some genetic tests reveal information about the potential of future ill health and disease, this may mean that some individuals are charged higher premiums or excluded from insurance all together, leading to social exclusion and the development of a 'genetic underclass'.

The concern for health professionals is that fear of discrimination, whether founded or not, may lead some people to avoid genetic testing altogether, with detrimental effects on their health. Professor John Burn of Clinical Genetics at University of Newcastle argued:

> If insurance companies are allowed access to genetic information people may avoid taking genetic tests that could save their lives for fear of not getting a mortgage or life insurance. Insurance companies will in effect be killing people (House of Commons Select Committee on Science and Technology, 1995).

This is rather a extreme statement, but there appears to be some evidence to support Burn's concerns. An NOP poll carried out on behalf of the Genetics Forum reported that three out of ten people who were questioned would not take a genetic test if faced with a disclosure requirement (Genetics Forum Opnion Poll, 1997). A survey carried out by Mintel Marketing Intelligence found that consumers recognise the benefits that genetic testing may bring to the management of inherited illnesses, but many are reluctant to take a test and will avoid insurers that request them (Mintel Marketing Intelligence, 1996). Another concern is that people may be encouraged to seek over-the-counter genetic tests in an attempt to avoid the results appearing on their medical records and thus being shared with their insurers.[1]

The Human Genetics Advisory Commission stated in their report that although they had received compelling anecdotal evidence of unreasonable discrimination, they had no hard evidence that this was systematic, and it remained unclear whether any discrimination was rare or common. The Commission concluded that '[d]espite inadequate quantitative evidence, we therefore could not set aside perceptions of unacceptable discrimination as groundless' (HGAC, 1997).

Professor Peter Harper has provided a useful summary of the key concerns which policy needs to address (shown in Box 6.1):

Box 6.1 – Principle concerns of insurers, applicants and professionals

Insurance companies
Adverse selection
Competition
Avoidance of unnecessary discrimination
Avoidance of adverse public opinion and legislation

Those at risk
Pressure to be tested to obtain basic life and health insurance
Confidentiality of high-risk result
Discrimination and stigmatisation after high-risk result
Wish to obtain insurance after low-risk result

Professional concerns
Testing of individuals who would otherwise prefer not to
Deterrence of those who would otherwise wish to be tested
Testing without adequate counselling
Testing minors
Stigmatisation of those with genetic diseases
Pressure for termination of affected pregnancies

Source: Harper and Clarke (1997) *Genetics, Society and Clinical Practice*, p51

Policy responses

Below we critically assess recent attempts to address these competing concerns, before setting out our suggestions for taking this debate forward.

The response in other countries

In the Netherlands there was a five year moratorium which banned insurance companies from using the results of information from genetic tests for applicants for life and private disability insurance for policies up to £81,300. This was recently reviewed by the Government, who subsequently asked the insurance companies to revise their policy of not covering those with a family history of muscular dystrophy or Huntington's disease (Human Genetics Advisory Commission, 1997).

Because the US health system is insurance-based, the failure to get insurance has much larger implications. A number of states have enacted laws to protect individuals from being denied health insurance on the basis on genetic information. Congress has passed a number of health care reforms including a provision that prevents US workers from being denied medical insurance on the basis of genetic information (Linnane, 1997; Charatan, 1997).

The response of the UK

The House of Commons Select committee which looked at the issue of human genetics and insurance in 1995, were dismayed at the industry's failure to address the issues raised by genetic testing:

> In our view the ABI has reacted to these predictions with undue complacency; it would, at least, be prudent to have contingency plans in place to ensure that changes were dealt with in an orderly manner ...The committee recommends that the insurance industry be allowed one year in which to propose a solution acceptable to Parliament, and that if it fails to do so a solution should be sought, by legislation if necessary.

On 17 July, 1996 just two days before the one year deadline imposed by the Select committee expired and a debate in the House of Commons on science policy and human genetics, the ABI announced the appointment of a genetics adviser, Professor Sandy Raeburn from the Department of Clinical Genetics at the University of Nottingham to help them develop a Code of Practice.

Code of Practice by the ABI

The ABI has recently published a Code of Practice which was drawn up by a Genetics Committee including individuals from outside the insurance industry with expertise in legal, ethical and social issues as well as insurance representatives. The aim of the Code is to govern the way insurers use, handle and store genetic test results, and is available in full from the ABI. The Code states that the results of genetic tests are not needed for most types of health, medical and critical illness insurance, and for life insurance below £100, 000 linked to house purchase loans. For life insurance policies above this figure, applicants will not be required to have a genetic test, but they will have to disclose any genetic test results which have already been carried out.

As part of their consultation on the Code of Practice, the ABI commissioned a citizens' jury to consider the issue of genetic testing and insurance in general and their draft Code of Practice in particular.[3]

Box 6.2 – Citizens' jury.

What is a citizens' jury?
Citizens' juries are an innovative attempt to involve the public in decisions which affect them in their own communities. A number of people are selected at random to reflect the local population. They sit for four days and are presented with evidence to help them reach a decision. People with a particular viewpoint or expertise are asked to speak to them and answer their questions. The jurors then discuss the issues amongst themselves and make recommendations which are submitted to the commissioning body in the form of a written report.

What were they asked?
'Should insurance companies continue to have access to the results to the results of genetic tests? What responsibilities do the insurance industry and government have for meeting the insurance needs of citizens?'

What did they recommend?
- Insurance companies should have access to *monogenetic* test results

- There should be a moratorium on the use of genetic tests for *multifactorial* diseases, which will be subject to review

- Generally welcomed the Code of Practice, suggesting several amendments

- There should be an independent body to monitor adherence to the CoP

- The Government should continue commitment to welfare state, particularly long-term care provision

The jury's key recommendations are summarised in box 6.2, but a full copy of their report, and a copy of the ABI's written response, is available on request from the ABI.

The Human Genetics Advisory Commission

At its first meeting, the Human Genetics Advisory Commission noted that the prospect of genetic testing for insurance merited early consideration. After taking evidence from actuaries, underwriters, the patient groups and clinicians, they produced a report at the end of 1997 entitled *The implications of genetic testing for insurance* (HGAC, 1997).

The HGAC concluded that it is unlikely that actuarially important genetic predictions of common causes of adult death will be available and validated for some time to come, as the information linking genetics and multifactorial disease is at too early a stage to make sound assessments of added risk. They also felt that the industry was capable of withstanding limited adverse selection.

Box 6.3 – Recommendations of HGAC

●   Industry should respect a two year moratorium on requiring disclosure of results of genetic tests, pending agreement that the actuarial base in relation to any particular test is secure.

●   Government should establish a mechanism to evaluate the scientific and actuarial evidence presented in support of specific genetic tests or insurance products. The burden of proof to justify lifting of any part of the moratorium should lie with the industry.

●   Government, in consultation with the industry and HGAC should consider how, and consider how the role of Financial Services Authority might be involved in the above.

●   Industry should consult with the Insurance Ombudsman and Consumer Protection groups to develop a robust independent appeals procedure.

Discussion

The Human Genetics Advisory Commission, as it title suggests, can only offer advice to Government. The Department of Trade and Industry has yet to respond to their report, but it is unusual for Ministers to ignore the advice of an expert body. While most of their recommendations are welcome, and remarkably similar to the views expressed by members of the citizens' jury, the report of the HGAC fails to differentiate between different types of genetic tests for different types of diseases. This is unfortunate, and leads us to question whether the recommendation for a moratorium on *all* genetic tests is justified or desirable.

In insurance, the debate has tended to centre around the competing claims of those who fear either adverse selection or discrimination, rather than a consideration of which (if any) types of genetic tests are relevant or appropriate to insurance. The distinction between diagnostic and predictive testing is important to this question. As Harper has noted, 'it is the predictive use of such tests in healthy individuals who may be at risk genetically that is the issue – not their use in the investigation of a person already ill' (Harper, 1997e). As pointed out in Chapter 1, there are two types of predictive genetic tests: presymptomatic and predispositional tests. Bearing these distinctions in mind, we need to ask ourselves the following questions:

- Which (if any) types of genetic tests are actuarially relevant – that is, provide quantifiable information about the relationship between having a gene and developing a disease?

- Which (if any) types of genetic tests will lead to unfair discrimination if insurance companies have access to them, and adverse selection if they don't?

Which types of genetic tests are actuarially relevant?

Professor Peter Harper explored this issue in his essay *Genetic testing and insurance*, where he concluded that the great majority of genetic disorders are of little or no relevance to the life insurance industry. Predictive testing for susceptibility genes is too uncertain in terms of risk prediction to be useful, as we do not yet fully understand the relationship between genes and illness in multifactorial diseases. Indeed, he points out that if the life insurance industry did persist in requiring all genetic tests to be declared, it would have to develop a complex system for assessing large amounts of data carried out largely for reproductive reasons and which are open to confusion and misinterpretation (Harper, 1997e).

These conclusions are similar to those reached by the Citizens' Jury (see box 6.2) who felt that the insurance industry should continue to have access to the results of presymptomatic tests for single gene disorders, but that there should be a moratorium on the results of Predispositional tests for multifactorial diseases, as the latter were not yet fully understood (ABI, 1997a).

Which types of genetic tests could lead to discrimination or adverse selection?

According to Harper's analysis, it is only the dominantly inherited disorders of late onset that are likely to be significant in terms of adverse selection. He lists eleven of these rare disorders, including: Huntington's disease, adult polycystic kidney disease, familial colon cancer and familial breast cancer. Harper points out that the great majority of these disorders occur within the context of a family history of the condition. Since most life insurance proposal forms request information about parents and are loaded accordingly, 'it is clear that the scope for such adverse selection is extremely limited' (Harper, 1997e). The family context of these disorders would also mean that applicants would not suffer from any greater discrimination if insurance companies had access to the results of a genetic test, as their premia would already have been loaded to take their family history into account.

Indeed, the citizens' jury which looked at genetic testing used this as an argument to justify allowing industry access to the results of single gene disorders such as Huntington's. Jurors argued that a negative test could benefit an applicant, who previously would have either been refused insurance or charged very high premiums in order to take into account their family history of this disease.

Policy implications

The HGAC called for a two year moratorium on insurance companies having access to all genetic tests.

> (disclosure) would only be acceptable when a quantifiable association between a given pattern of test results and events actuarially relevant for a specific insurance product had been established (HGAC, 1997).

However, it would seem that a small number of genetic tests for single gene disorders of late onset already meets this criteria. There is a clear consensus that predictive testing for susceptibility genes is too uncertain in terms of risk prediction to be used by the insurance industry. Yet, as Harper has warned, this could change quickly, which points to the need to resolve the more clear cut issues involving Monogenic diseases now, so that we can go on to discuss the more complex issues raised by predispositional tests when and if they arise.

The HGAC report pointed to the lack of real evidence either way of adverse selection or discrimination in the insurance industry. A blanket moratorium on all forms of genetic tests would not fill this information gap, and will take us no further in the debate. In two years time, we will still be debating the problems of privacy and access in the absence of any real evidence to support either side. Limited access to carefully defined tests, which would be the subject of an independent monitoring body could provide an invaluable source of evidence to help identify best practice and guide future policy development. In addition to the recommendations of the HGAC, which we support, we therefore recommend that:

●   Government impose a general moratorium on genetic test results, but consider an exception for certain genetic tests such as dominantly inherited single gene disorders of late onset

●   The independent monitoring body (as recommended by the HGAC and the citizens' jury) should ensure that the moratorium is respected and monitor how the test results covered by the exemption are treated and with what effect

• The above would provide invaluable evidence to inform the work of the evaluation mechanism recommended by the HGAC to consider actuarial evidence presented in support of specific genetic tests or insurance products.

The HGAC called for an early dialogue between the Government and the industry to promote a shared view (HGAC, 1997). A general moratorium with carefully defined exceptions, subject to appropriate monitoring and review systems may offer a realistic way of achieving this aim.

Genetic information and employers

The issue of whether insurance companies should have access to genetic information has received wide spread coverage in the media and provoked much debate. The potential use of genetic information by employers, in comparison, has not attracted much interest. Yet this issue has equal, if not greater potential to affect public perception of the new genetics. Not every person will take out life insurance, but the majority of adults depend upon employment to survive.

It may be that where there is no smoke, there is no fire. The Nuffield Council on Bioethics found no evidence of UK or USA employers demanding genetic screening before reaching a decision on the employability of individuals. But as McLean has pointed out, just because such events are not happening yet, this does not mean that they never will (McLean, 1994). In the UK there is currently no law which would preclude employers from making such demands on actual or potential employees, and there are no legal safeguards in place to prevent abuse. Given the predicted pace of developments in genetic testing, the absence of any legislative framework to respond to the challenges ahead is a matter for concern.

The House of Commons Select Committee which looked at the issue of whether employers should have access to the results of genetic tests stated: 'As a general principle, we agree with the Clinical Molecular Genetics Society that decisions on employment should be based on current ability to do the job'. They then proceeded to outline two possible exceptions to this rule. The first exception is that if there is a danger that others may be put at risk. Although the Committee acknowledged that there is no known genetic diagnosis sufficiently robust to make a case for insisting that it be revealed to an employer, they suggested that it would be appropriate to know that an airline pilot could suffer from a heart attack before 55. The second possibility is that genetic testing may, in time, tell us if an individual is likely to be more sensitive than many others to the environmental effects of particular substances.

This second point, that there may be evidence that an individual is more sensitive than others to particular substances raises a number of concerns, and threatens a fundamental shift in responsibility for health and safety from the employer to the individual employee. Let us take the example of workers who may be exposed to asbestos, and imagine the impact of such policies on the individual in particular and health and safety as a whole. Mesothelioma is a rare terminal cancer of the pleura caused by asbestos exposure. Unlike other lung diseases, there is no causal link with smoking. Not everybody exposed to asbestos develops this cancer and some reports have suggested that certain members of the population may be more susceptible than others to developing this fatal disease.

If an employer in an industry which involved asbestos exposure was allowed to screen out people susceptible to this particular cancer, what would be the consequences? Firstly, there is a danger of creating a genetic underclass of manual workers who are excluded from the work in which they are skilled. Asbestos is present in over a thousand products, and it would be unlikely that a manual worker would not come into contact with it at some point (Lenaghan, 1993).[4] Secondly, and most importantly, a product like asbestos is present in most buildings, friction materials, as well as many household items such as ironing boards. The excluded worker will find it difficult to avoid contact with asbestos in his personal life. The problem will have been shifted to the individual, the number and cost of asbestos-related diseases linked to the industry will be limited and the pressure to ban a carcinogen which affects us all will have been significantly reduced.

As the TUC has warned:

> Without statutory protection against discrimination (the Disability Discrimination Act does not cover people with a predispostion to a disease or condition) less scrupulous

employers might use tests to exclude from employment people with a genetic predisposition to a condition. They could then use the fact that the workforce was less likely than previously to suffer that condition to justify reductions on health and safety provision (TUC Equal Rights Department, 1997).

These problems are not just related to asbestos. The majority of exposures to hazardous substances occur in manual jobs. However, the professional classes could also be affected if employers were allowed access to the results of genetic tests. As Sheila McLean has noted, it would be tempting for some to look at the genetic make up of potential medical students, before investing in a seven year training programme, which could be 'wasted' if the person had a poor genetic profile.

Policy responses

After considering the issues raised by insurance, employment and genetic testing, the House of Commons Select Committee concluded that:

> In our view, the fundamental question is not about genetic information per se, but about personal privacy ...If genetic information were treated as private to the person concerned, and if there were adequate sanctions for breach of privacy then there would be few problems of discrimination.

The Committee observed that it is possible to obtain material for genetic testing from a single hair root – and in light of the reporting of the HIV status of stars in the 1980s 'misuse of genetic information should be both a criminal and a civil offence, since revelation of genetic information could have devastating effects'. They felt that this would give greater protection than simply defining genetic susceptibility to disease as a disability under the terms of the Disability Discrimination Act.

However, the Human Genetics Advisory Commission felt that the evidence which they collected did not support the argument that there should be an absolute right of privacy for knowledge of genetic tests, but do not explain why (HGAC, 1997).[5] The issue of privacy law is a complex one and is beyond the remit of this publication to debate the pros and cons of legislation in this area. However, it is an approach which certainly warrants further consideration and debate, particularly when and if genetic testing becomes more widespread.

It would be unfortunate if it took a few unscrupulous employers to force a public policy reaction. It is not just individual employees who would suffer, but the perception of genetic tests as a whole. We therefore recommend the following action as a matter of urgency:

- The issue of genetic information and employers needs to be put much higher on the public policy agenda

- The current lack of any legal safeguards against abuse is a cause for concern

- Means for preventing or managing employer access to genetic information should be explored, such as privacy laws

- Trade unions and employer organisations should be included in these vital debates

Future issues

Many of the dilemmas discussed above represent our reaction to and understanding of the genetic tests which are currently available. However, as we have repeated throughout this report, the new genetics is a fast moving area of knowledge. Developments in the availability and application of predictive genetic tests, combined with changes in the role of the welfare state will raise important questions about the nature of our society and the responsibilities which individual citizens have for themselves and each other.

> Insurance, whether for health or for life is an important feature of the world in which we live ...It is a necessity of life for many people, but it also highlights very clearly the potential tensions between the individual and the community (McLean, 1997a).

These are complex issues, and below we flag up some questions which are likely to increasingly feature in future policy debates.

Long term care

It is unfortunate that much of the debate around insurance and genetics has focused on life insurance, and that so little attention has been given to insurance for long term care (LTC), which is likely to be of increasing importance in the UK. When the Welfare State was founded, the NHS provided health care for the sick and infirm free at the point of use. Local authorities provided long-term social care on a means-tested basis. However, the predicted growth in the number of dependent elderly people have led politicians to seriously consider alternative funding options for long term care (Coote & Hunter, 1996). The previous government encouraged the growth of a commercial insurance sector in LTC. The current government has set up a Royal Commission to consider various options, which is due to report at the end of this year.

Alzheimer's disease is increasingly relevant in the context of long term care insurance and genetic testing (Pokorski, 1998). The consequences of predictive genetic tests for disorders of old age such as Alzheimer's disease could be disastrous if we move to a system of private insurance for LTC. Those who are identified as being at higher risk of developing such diseases, and therefore are most likely to need insurance for long term care, would effectively be priced out of the market. A National Study Group has claimed that genetic tests would be used by industry to avoid insuring higher-risk individuals (Post *et al*, 1997).

As a society, we may feel it is not just unfair but intolerable if some individuals are unable to obtain care for their basic needs. However, as Pokorski has noted, the suggested remedy, preventing insurers from using genetic tests is in effect calling for an entitlement to buy LTC insurance regardless of one's likelihood to claim. 'The problem with this proposal is that private insurance is voluntary. *Consumers* enter and leave the market at will' (my italics) (Pokorski, 1998).

Whereas access to long term care was once paid for collectively, and available to all, it is now a matter for individual responsibility, and therefore the rules of the market operate. Interestingly, it is insurers, rather than user groups, that have been most vocal in drawing attention to these developments. John Hylands of Standard Life, in his evidence to the citizens' jury pointed out that his company does not offer LTC products, as they do not believe that private insurance can meet people's needs in this area. Long term care, he argued, is an example where the solidarity, rather than the mutuality principle should operate (ABI, 1997a).

Arguing for private insurance companies not to have access to genetic data rather misses the point. If we do not want people to be priced out of the market for long term care (or indeed other forms of insurance), then we need to explore the means for creating a social insurance system that is compulsory, universal and based upon the principle of solidarity.

Pokorski refers to the philosopher John Rawls, who asserted that all citizens have fundamental rights as a matter of social justice, and concludes:

> Policy-makers must decide if insurance is one of those rights, and if so, which types of cover should be provided. They must then find ways of satisfying these obligations (Pokorski, 1998).

An inclusive or divisive society?

Much of this chapter has been concerned with the potential for insurers to discriminate against individuals, but what if genetic data was used in *favour* of the applicant? The Human Genetics Advisory Commission identified concerns that insurers may identify a subgroup with lower-than-average risks and offer them lower premiums or 'preferred life' terms. Consequently, the poorer risks would be left paying higher premiums or might become uninsurable (HGAC, 1997).

Although there is no evidence of this practice yet, (indeed, the ABI has explicitly ruled it out), 'cherry picking' is a common feature of house and motor insurance. It is important to remember that insurance companies are commercial companies, whose aim is to make a profit. It is not the responsibility of private insurance companies to ensure equity within society. They are in competition with other companies, and therefore must remain competitive or fail. If one company begins to offer preferred life policies, then others will inevitably follow.

The extent to which cherry picking develops may depend upon the level of public demand. Once people begin to know more about their own genetic make-up, will the healthy be more or less willing to subsidise the costs caused by the unhealthy?

The editor of *Nature* has argued that:

> The contention that people unlucky enough to carry identifiable genetic abnormality should not be denied insurance on the same terms as other people, begs the question why people relatively free from identifiable genetic abnormality should therefore pay more than would otherwise be necessary (Maddox, 1991).

At the moment, this is just a lone voice, but if widespread genetic testing develops, this may encourage increasing numbers to ask the same question. Genetics may have the power not just to transform our ability to diagnose and treat disease, but alter our very concepts of what constitutes public and private responsibilities. Some people have already begun to question whether those who are 'responsible' for their own illnesses, such as smokers, should receive care from the NHS. Will the new genetics encourage a more divisive trend in our society?

However, McLean reminds us not be too pessimistic when considering the impact of genetics on discrimination:

> Elementary genetic knowledge will also show that no-one is free from some genetic deviation – indeed, it may well reinforce the fact that there is no norm from which deviation is possible. If this is possible, if this is so, it may also have a profound impact on the potential for discrimination (McLean, 1997a)

McLean provides a welcome reminder that pessimism in the face of the new genetics is both unwarranted and inappropriate. If genetics has the potential to show us how we differ from one another, it can also reveal to us what we share. The Welfare State was created in the aftermath of the second world war, by a generation who learnt that we can achieve more together than we can alone. Some of these principles have been lost or forgotten in the past two decades, as the line between public and private responsibilities has blurred. The new knowledge offered by genetics may remind us once more of the commonality of all our fates.

Summary of issues and recommendations

Insurance companies and genetic information

The question of whether insurance companies should have access to genetic test results is likley to influence public perception of and demand for genetic services in the future. Industry fears that without access to test results they will suffer adverse selection. Health professionals and user groups have expressed fears that if industry docs have access, then the public could suffer genetic discrimination, resulting in a low uptake of tests of potential benefit. However, little evidence exists to support either side. In this chapter we argued that too little attention had been paid to the distinction between different types of tests and diseases, and recommended that:

- Government impose a general moratorium on genetic test results, but consider an exception for a small number of certain genetic tests such as dominantly inherited single gene disorders of late onset.

- The independent monitoring body (as recommended by the HGAC and the citizens' jury) should ensure that the moratorium is respected and monitor how the test results covered by the exemption are treated and with what effect.

- The above would provide invaluable evidence to inform the work of the evaluation mechanism recommended by the HGAC to consider actuarial evidence presented in support of specific genetic tests or insurance products.

Employers and genetic information

Too little attention has been given to the potential for discrimination if employers are allowed access to genetic information. There is currently no legislation in place to prevent possible abuse. We therefore recommend:

- The issue of genetic information and employers needs to be put much higher on the public policy agenda

- The current lack of any legal safeguards against abuse is a cause for concern

- Means for preventing or managing employer access to genetic information should be explored, such as privacy laws

- Trade unions and employer organisations should be included in these vital debates

Future issues

In the final section of this chapter we highlighted areas for future discussion and research. IPPR will continue to explore the issue of rights and responsibilities in health care, but meanwhile, we raise the following issues:

- We need a public debate to decide which risks should be a matter for individual responsibility and which should be shared

- Policy makers must develop mechanisms that allow risk to be shared where appropriate, such as social insurance systems for long term care

- Policy makers and politicians must strive to develop and encourage policies that emphasise what unites us, and not leave the market to use genetics to divide us.

Endnotes

1   The ACGT has stated that all commerical companies offering genetic tests should ensure that the results are shared with the patient's GP, following their consent. This issue is discussed in Chapter 5.

2   One of the most comprehensive laws protecting genetic information, The Genetic Privacy Act, passed in New Jersey declares that: 'A person's genetic information is private property and cannot be collected, retained or disclosed without written consent. Employers cannot refuse to hire anyone who declines to take a genetic test and health insurance companies cannot deny access or set higher rates for people who are genetically predisposed to certain diseases'. Charatan F B (1997) 'New Jersey passes genetic privacy bill', *BMJ*, 313, p.71, 13 July.

3   IPPR has been at the forefront of developing this method in the UK, and we were commissioned in conjuction with Opinion Leader Research to carry out a jury on genetics and insurance for the ABI. A summary of the process and findings is contained in box 6.2, but a full copy of the report is available from the Association of British Insurers, together with their written response.

4   This report contains a full analysis and discussion of the discrimination faced by workers with asbestos-related diseases and much of the information on the following pages draws from this study.

5   They were generally satisfied with the arrangements for maintaining confidentiality of data which might include genetic data. However, they recommended that the Data Protection Registrar keep under review the ways in which insurers collect and handle genetic test results.

7. For the future

This publication was written in an effort to begin to bridge a perceived policy gap between the technological, organisational and cultural changes taking place within and without the National Health Service. We have attempted to demystify the relationship between genes and disease and to highlight some of the issues which the new genetics will raise for the NHS over the next decade. However, this report represents the beginning, rather than the end, of an important debate. Whilst we have tried to cover comprehensively the most immediate issues which the health service needs to address, we are conscious that we are unable to do justice to all aspects of the debate.

In this final chapter, we identify issues which were beyond the capacity of this report, but which merit further debate and research in the years to come. Below we consider the potential costs of the new genetics, and the factors that are likely to influence the final bill, such as the patenting of genes. We briefly assess the role of public demand, and the related issue of public education. Finally, we consider the increasingly complex relationship between the media, science, uncertainty and public policy. We conclude by repeating the need for a coherent set of principles to guide the NHS in the future, and highlight the need for policy makers to plan for uncertainty.

Can we afford the new genetics?

One of the key concerns about the future development of genetics, like many other new technologies, is cost. Unfortunately, there is very little data on the anticipated costs of future genetic services. This is partly due to the fact that the cost of the service will depend upon a variety of different and interacting factors. A key influence is likely to be the level of public demand for both genetic services and counselling. Other important factors are likely to include the extent to which we develop the ability to automate genetic technologies, and the impact of patents. Each of these aspects of the future cost of genetic services are discussed briefly below, but require further research.

Technology and cost

The second report of the Genetics Research Advisory Committee noted that most commercial gene tests cost between $200–$500 each, warning:

> ... hence large screening programmes would put an enormous burden on the NHS. The costs of these tests can only be reduced by new technologies involving substantial automation. The outcome of the current struggles to patent orphan DNA sequences may have a crucial influence on the ultimate prices of screening tests (Department of Health, 1995).

The same report predicted that it is unlikely that substantial automation techniques will be generally available to the NHS in the next five years. Although advances in biotechnology could initially lead to more expensive treatments, we should not fall prey to crude, ball park figures which do not sufficiently analyse the full economic and social benefits. Developments in genetics may have the potential to reduce, as well as raise, health care costs. Arguably, more effective targeting of drugs on the right patients could save resources, particularly if treatment avoids lengthy inpatient stays or alleviates the more severe symptoms in chronic diseases (Hunter, 1998).

Several health economists have questioned the assumption that new technologies in the NHS must always drive up costs, pointing to the fact that as with all new technologies, there is a learning curve, whereby as the intervention becomes more common place, the technology becomes cheaper (Donaldson, 1996).

Counselling and cost

There is one aspect of genetic services which may have the potential to significantly increase cost pressures: the need and/or demand for genetic counselling. As we noted in Chapter 2, there is a professional consensus that most genetic tests and screening programmes should be accompanied by pre and post test counselling. This may involve not just the individual initially concerned, but family members also. Counselling is potentially expensive as it requires a great deal of time from skilled professionals, who at the moment are a scarce resource.

The extent to which this becomes a problem for the NHS depends upon how many trained counsellors we have in the future, and how (if at all) we educate and train other NHS professionals such as GPs and nurses to perform or share these functions. Counselling should ideally be a part of all clinical consultations, but as noted in chapter 4, time is a scarce resource in primary care, and GPs may have little skills or tolerance of communicating probabilistic information. The level of counselling required may also depend upon the degree to which the general public understands the relationship between genes and diseases. The issue of public education is discussed in more detail below.

Patents and cost

The patenting of human genes is one of the most contentious issues in biotechnology. A patent is a monopoly right, granted for a limited period to an inventor in return for the publication of the details of the invention. The requirements for patentability are: novelty, inventiveness, industrial applicability, sufficiency of description and the absence of any feature that makes for inherent unpatentability. (Nuffield Council on Bioethics, 1993).

In March 1995, the European parliament rejected the European Directive on Biotechnology which would have allowed for the 'legal protection of biotechnological inventions'. The Directive had taken seven years to debate, in the European Commission, the Council of Ministers and the European Parliament. However, at the time of writing, the European Directive is due to receive its second reading, and a successful conclusion seems virtually guaranteed.

Initially the European Parliament's main objection to the patenting of genes was for ethical reasons. They argued that it is unethical to patent a life form because it reduces life to a mere commodity. MEPs claimed that genes cannot be invented: they can only be discovered, and that one of the main reasons for granting patents – to act as a spur to others to produce something better – cannot apply to genes because a gene cannot be improved.

While not disputing the importance of this debate, it is unfortunate that so much of this discussion has focused around ethical issues, and so little has centred on the practical implications of patenting for the NHS. There are two areas where the issue of patenting is immediately relevant to the health service: research and development (R&D) and the costs of new services. Below we briefly outline the main issues which patenting raises in these areas, in the hope of provoking a wider (albeit belated) debate in the NHS on these important issues.

Those in favour of patenting genes draw attention to the fact that research and development in health in general and in genetics in particular is expensive. If companies cannot recoup the money they have invested by up to 20 years of patent protection, then commercial companies claim that they will not invest in research, and therefore new discoveries will not be made. They also claim that patenting actually encourages scientists to be more open about their achievements because they have to publish the details of a patent.

Those against patenting claim that patents actually discourages research, because researchers are either reluctant or unable to pay for work if a key element of the basic knowledge is already owned by a competitor. Charities which have spent millions of pounds on research could find themselves paying royalties on screening kits to US research groups, even though the discovery of the gene may be built on the work of the whole research community (Nature, 1997c).

It has also been claimed that patenting increases the costs of health care. As the Genetic Interest Group warned:

> There is a problem associated with genetic patenting that has not received an airing. To date much emphasis has been given to the issues created by patenting of genes for single gene disorders. In the case of conditions where multifactorial inheritance applies, costs will mount if payments have to be made to each and every discoverer of a gene contributing to the overall predisposition to develop a specific condition (HCSCST, 1995).

The Department of Health has also expressed caution about the effect of patenting on the ultimate price of genetic tests (Department of Health, 1995). In our view, it is regrettable that companies may now be allowed to patent genes. The issues raised in terms of research and cost are of real concern to the NHS. A full consideration of these issues is beyond the scope of this report, but we urge more research and debate about how the NHS can avoid the possible negative consequences outlined above. Individual laboratories have little bargaining power, collective approaches in which, for example, negotiations with suppliers may be conducted on their behalf by the NHS Executive, should be explored.

The problem for policy makers is that there are actually very few good studies of the cost of the new genetic technologies. There is an urgent need to develop proper analyses of the full cost of genetic services, taking into account the potential impact of patents, public demand and counselling. Such information is essential in order to allow the NHS to plan for the future. The dangers of applying a crude cost-benefit analysis to genetics was discussed in Chapter 3. Any such analyses must include the views of the user, and a more holistic approach to assessing the costs and benefits of health care in general.

Public demand

The level of public demand for genetic tests and screening programmes will play a crucial role in the future development and costs of genetic services, and may depend upon a complex combination of factors, including public knowledge and perception of genetics in general and of each disease and test in particular. The nature of the disorder, the age at which it symptoms develop, the treatments that may or may not be available, how the disorder is inherited, the availability of genetic information to insurance companies and employers are all likely to be important factors in shaping future demand.

Recent experience shows that the level of public demand for a genetic test can be difficult to predict accurately. For example, before a test for Huntington's disease became available, 80 per cent of those with a family history thought that they would like to know their status. However, when the test became available, only ten per cent took advantage of this test. This can be contrasted with the case of breast cancer for which there is a very high (and some would say inappropriate) demand, even though approximately only five per cent of all breast cancers are inherited. Breast cancer is a common disease, affecting one in 12 women. There is a high level of awareness of the disease amongst the general public, and extensive media coverage. It is possible that the demand for testing may well be in excess of what is actually required (see Chapter 2).

For policy makers, the question is, do we attempt to educate and persuade women that *BRCA1/2* testing is only likely to provide useful information for a very small group of people, thus reducing 'inappropriate demand' for this test, or we do attempt to understand and respond to lay perceptions of risk, and develop services accordingly? If we embark upon a programme of public education, what message should be communicated, by whom, and to what end?

Public education

The general standard of knowledge about genetics has been much lamented, and there have been frequent calls for programmes to increase public awareness of the role of genes in disease. Establishing genetics as part of the national curriculum and encouraging a wider debate in society have all been proposed at various times as key to this process. But what are we trying to achieve? And is 'public education' the right approach?

There are three reasons usually cited to justify or warrant public education programmes:

● to provide a foundation for counselling

● to reduce the cost/need for counselling

● to enable the public to participate in wider debates about the future development of genetic technologies.

Sir Walter Bodmer has argued that firstly, understanding of genetics would create 'the substrate for a better ability to receive the advice that counselling involves'. This would seem eminently sensible and desirable, although in this model, the patient appears to be a passive recipient of information. A broader understanding of genetics in society would ideally allow individuals to not just receive, but to question and engage with the advice and information which NHS professionals might give them. This would enable individuals to become actively involved in their own care regimes.

It has also been suggested that public education is important from an economic perspective, as it could be central to the cost-effective development of services. The Department of Health has claimed:

It will be logistically and economically impossible to provide one-to one counselling to cover multiple risks for large numbers of people offered new screening tests (Department of Health, 1995).

This argument is backed up by the experience of Mediterranean genetics programmes, which indicate that the better the community is informed, the less need there is for time consuming and expensive face-to-face counselling (WHO, 1991). However, whilst this argument might be appealing to a cash-strapped NHS, it cannot be the only justification for a public education programme. The decision about whether to provide counselling or not should be made upon the basis of need, not cost. If the resources (whether human or financial) to meet this need do not exist, then other ways of providing them must be explored. A general public education programme is desirable, but it is not an acceptable substitute for a high quality and comprehensive genetic counselling service.

The third reason why the public should be educated as to the nature of genetic technology and the choices such knowledge will impose is, according to Sir Walter Bodmer that:

Such knowledge may change society. If changes occur they will doubtless be hotly debated in the media but the general public should have the basic knowledge that is needed to allow them to participate and listen intelligently to debate (House of Commons Select Committee 1995).

Therefore, the public needs a greater understanding of genetics not just in order to help them make choices within their own individual lives and families, but to enable them to participate in debates about the wider use of genetics in society generally. This is perhaps the most important objective of any public education programme. As the House of Commons Select Committee stated:

The dilemmas that genetics pose will be resolved by the public and parliamentary debate, not by academics alone. But that debate must be well informed, both about the science itself and about its ethical, legal and social implications (House of Commons Select Committee, 1995).

The committee made several recommendations as to how genetic knowledge could form part of the national curriculum, which the Wellcome Trust is taking forward. Other innovative methods have recently being explored, including citizens' juries (Coote & Lenaghan, 1997). There have been three citizens' juries in the UK so far on issues raised by genetics including genetics and insurance (see Chapter 6) genetic services and the NHS (Welsh Institute for Health and Social Care, 1998) and the genetic modification of food. Citizens' juries may be a useful (but certainly not the only) method for facilitating informed debate on these vital issues. The Human Genetics Advisory Commission has a remit to encourage a public debate about genetics, which it has done through a series of public meetings. Sweden has recently held a referendum on the genetic modification of food. Other initiatives include the Gene Shop at Manchester Airport. There is a need for independent evaluation of all of these methods, to assess just how effective each approach in provoking an informed and wide public debate.

However, we should not assume that an educated public would support research or innovation uncritically. Uninformed hostility can turn to informed opposition, based upon well founded social and/or economic arguments. But a well-informed public should be better able to voice their concerns and have them addressed by policy makers.

It is equally important not to assume that the provision of education will result in 'rational' behaviour. Research into public perceptions and reactions to genetic risk reveals repeated patterns of 'irrationality, inconsistency, and incompetence in the ways human beings arrive at decisions and choices when faced with uncertainty' (Kahneman and Tversky, 1986). These issues are discussed in detail in *The Troubled Helix* (Marteau and Richards, 1996).

Public perceptions of and reactions to risk may not necessarily be 'wrong' but merely *different* to those of professionals. It is important that policy makers understand the ways in which the public may react to the potential choices offered by the new genetics, as this could have profound implications for the uptake and development of genetic services as a whole. It has been suggested that the choices people make as a result of genetic tests or screening programmes should be reported and analysed, in order to help the future development of genetic services (WHO, 1991).

The media, science and public policy

It is increasingly futile to talk about the need for public education or public perceptions of risk without considering one of the most important influences of the late twentieth century: the media. Modern life is an increasingly socially mediated experience, one in which systems of mass communications, both printed and electronic, play a key role. As such, the media has the power not only to inform the public of the challenges and opportunities presented by genetic knowledge, but also shape people's perceptions of developments, either by coverage or omission. Professor David Hunter has written that in any debate about genetics, the media must be included in the list of stakeholders, as '[a] proper understanding on its part of the complex issues involved is critical if public debate is to be informed rather than sensationalised' (Hunter, 1998).

Many scientists who gave evidence to the House of Commons Select Committee on Human Genetics felt that the public misunderstood what they were trying to do, and indeed, what was possible. This, they felt, was fuelled by the media, who tend to report science in terms of 'breakthroughs' without sufficient caveats about the difficulties and time involved. The media, they claimed, tend to give a deterministic view of genetics, despite the fact that there are few certainties and causal links in all but a handful of diseases. Others pointed out that some scientists are also to blame, as they appear willing to exploit the media in return for the oxygen of publicity. The committee somewhat naively concluded:

> While scientists should make greater efforts to render their work intelligible, the media, for their part, should become more willing to report the steady progress of research and discuss the issues arising from that research in a more responsible way than is presently the case (HCSCST, 1995).

As Karpf has written, the media can play both a mystificatory and de-mystificatory role in relation to modern medicine. The question is, how can we encourage the latter? Mere exhortation from parliamentary committees is unlikely to be enough. IPPR will be exploring the complex relationship between the media and public perception of health issues in the forthcoming year. However, it is important to recognise that we have a problem not just with how the media interprets genetics in particular, but with how public policy responds to science and questions of uncertainty in general.

Public policy in conditions of uncertainty

The recent case of BSE demonstrated the choice which decision makers face between media and public allegations of 'scare mongering' and public allegations of 'cover ups'. It is difficult to chart a rational way in such circumstances. Giddens and most notably Beck have written about the relationship between the public and science (Franklin, 1998). The sureties of tradition and custom have not been replaced by rational knowledge; instead doubt has become a pervasive feature of modern critical reasoning. As Giddens argues, in these circumstances of increasing reflexivity, uncertainty and choice, the notions of trust and risk become particularly pertinent.

For Coote, the implications of what Beck has called the 'risk society' for the conduct of public policy making is that we must develop an adult-to-adult relationship with politicians and experts, where we respect each others knowledge and experience. Equally important, argues Coote, is the need for policy makers to become skilled at planning for uncertainty:

> It is futile to predict ... how genetics and biotechnology will change the face of the National Health Service, or the health of the population ...Planning for uncertainty involves a clear understanding of the principles that guide policy making. We may not know the shape of things to come or where we want to end up, but we can decide how we are going to travel, and why (Coote, 1998).

This takes us back to where we started in Chapter 1, where we outlined just how uncertain we are about the likely pace and nature of future developments in genetics. Experts disagree, vested interests compete to push their view, and it is difficult for policy makers to separate rhetoric from reality.

The greater the degree of uncertainty about the future, the greater the need for us to have an open and explicit debate about the principles and aims of the National Health Service. In our view, the NHS must maintain and strengthen its commitment to provide a comprehensive health service, free at the point of delivery and available to all on the basis of need and need alone. Health professionals must strive to ensure that the health service remains a tool for reducing, not increasing inequality in our society. Policy makers must ensure that the NHS continues to operate in the interests of all citizens, not in response to the demands of vocal or wealthy consumers. The NHS must remain in the driving seat of change, so that industry serves the needs of the British public, and not the other way round.

Just as the genie escaped from the bottle, the gene is now out of the test tube and we cannot put it back. Our best hope is to keep talking, loud and clear, so that everyone can hear. An open, explicit and inclusive debate on the future development on genetics is essential, so that we can all participate in shaping the Brave New NHS.

References

Association of British Insurers (1997a) *Citizens' Jury Report*, December 1997.

Association of British Insurers (1997b) *Life Insurance and Genetics: A Policy Statement*, 18 December.

Advisory Committee on Genetic Testing (1997) *Code of Practice and Guidance on Human Genetic Testing Services Supplied Directly to the Public*, Department of Health.

Advisory Committee on Genetic Testing (1998) *Consultation report on genetic testing for late onset disorders*, Department of Health.

Bell J (1998) 'The new genetics in clinical practice', *BMJ*, 316, pp.618-20.

BMA (1992) *Our Genetic Future: The Science and Ethics of Genetic Technology*, Oxford University Press.

Charatan F B (1997) 'New Jersey passes genetic privacy bill', *BMJ*, 313, p.71.

Clarke AJ (1997a) 'The genetic testing of children' in Harper PS & Clarke *Genetics, Society and Clinical Practice* BIOS Scientific Publishers, Oxford, pp.15-31.

Clarke AJ (1997b) 'Newborn screening' in Harper PS & Clarke AJ *op cit.*, Oxford pp.107-119.

Clarke AJ (1997c) 'Population screening for genetic carrier status' in Harper PS & Clarke AJ, *op cit.*, pp.77-93.

Clarke AJ (1997d) 'Prenatal genetic screening: paradigms and perspective in Harper PS & Clarke *op cit.*, pp.119-141.

Clarke AJ (1997e) 'A note on inheritance', appendix to Population screening for genetic carrier status in Harper PS & Clarke AJ, *op cit.*, p.91.

Conway S (1998) 'Greater Expectations in Managers and Medicine', *Health Service Journal*, 30 April.

Coote A (1998) 'Risk and Public Policy: Towards a high trust democracy' in Franklin J *The Politics of Risk Society*, Polity Press.

Coote A & Hunter D (1996) *A New Agenda For Health*, IPPR, London.

Coote A & Lenaghan J (1997) *Citizens' juries: Theory into practice*, IPPR, London.

Department of Health (1997) *The New NHS. Modern. Dependable*, HMSO, London.

Department of Health Press Release (1996) *New National Screening Committee Announced*, 17 July.

Department of Health (1998) *Our Healthier Nation*, HMSO, London.

Department of Health Press Release (1998a) *First report of the National Screening Committee*, 21 April.

Department of Health Press Release (1998b) *Alan Milburn announces new planning frameworks for rare condition services*, 16 April.

Donaldson C (1996) *Can we afford the NHS?*, IPPR, London.

Duggan M (1995) *Primary Health Care: a prognosis*, IPPR, London.

Fox J (1998) 'Computers, decision making and clinical effectiveness' in Lenaghan J (ed) *Rethinking IT and Health*, IPPR, London.

Franklin J (1997) *The Politics of Risk Society*, Polity Press, Cambridge.

Geller G & Holzman N (1991) 'Implications of the Human Genome Initiative of the Primary Care Physician', *Bioethics*, 5(4).

Genetics Forum Opnion Poll (1997) *Spice of Life*, 5(5)

Genetic Interest Group (1995) *The Present Organisation of Genetic Services in the United Kingdom*, a report by the Genetic Interest Group.

Genetic Interest Group (1997) *Commercialisation of Genetic Testing*, a report by the Genetic Interest Group.

Genetic Interest Group (1998) *Confidentiality and Medical Genetics*, a report by the Genetic Interest Group.

Genetics Research Advisory Group (1995a) *A first report to the NHS Central Research and Development Committee on the new genetics*, Department of Health, HMSO, London.

Genetic Research Advisory Group (1995b) *A second report to the NHS Central Research and Development Committee on the new genetics*, Department of Health, HMSO, London.

Ham C (1997) *Health Care Reform*, Open University Press, Buckingham.

Harper PS & Clarke AJ (1997) *Genetics, Society and Clinical Practice*, BIOS Scientific publishers, Oxford.

Harper PS (1997a) 'What do we mean by genetic testing?' in Harper PS & Clarke AJ *op cit.*, pp.7-15.

Harper PS (1997b) 'Presymptomatic testing for late-onset genetic disorders' in Harper PS & Clarke AJ *op cit.*, pp.31-49.

Harper PS (1997c) 'Genetics and public health' in Harper PS & Clarke AJ *op cit.*, pp.143-149.

Harper PS (1997d) 'Over the counter genetic testing' in Harper PS & Clarke AJ *op cit.*, pp.67-75.

Harper PS (1997e) 'Genetic testing and insurance' in Harper PS & Clarke AJ *op cit.*, pp.49-66.

Harris H, Scotcher D, Hartley N, Wallace A, Craufurd D & Harris R (1993) 'Cystic fibrosis carrier testing in early pregnancy by general practitioners', *BMJ*, 306.

Harris R (1991) 'The new genetics: a challenge to traditional medicine', *Journal of the Royal College of Physicians*, 25(2).

Holtzman NA & Shapiro D (1998) 'Genetic testing and public policy', *BMJ*, 316, pp.852-856.

House of Commons Select Committee on Science and Technology (1996) *Human Genetics: The Science and its Consequences*, HMSO, London.

Hubbard R & Lewontin RC (1996) 'Pitfalls of genetic testing', *The New England Journal of Medicine*, 2 May, pp.1192-1193.

Human Genetics Advisory Commission (1997) *The implications of genetic testing for insurance*, Department of Trade and Industry, HMSO, London.

Human Genetics Advisory Commission (1998) *First Annual Report*, Department of Trade and Industry, HMSO, London.

Hunter D (1998) Genning up on genetics, *Health Service Journal*, 3 September, p.16.

Kinmonth LK, Reinhard J, Bobrow M & Pauker S (1998) 'Implications for clinical services in Britain and the United States', *BMJ*, 316, pp.767-770.

Klein (1997) *King's Fund News*, 20(1), Spring 1997.

Lenaghan J (1993) *Victims Twice Over*, Clydeside Action on Asbestos, Glasgow.

Lenaghan J (1996) *Rationing and Rights in Health Care*, IPPR, London.

Linnane E (1996) 'Genetic testing: an ethical problem for priority setting', *British Journal of Health Care Management*, 2 (12).

MacDonald AS (1997) 'How will improved forecasts of individual lifetimes affect underwriting?', *Transactions of the Royal Society*, 352, pp.1067-1075.

Macer DRJ (1990) *Shaping genes*, Eubios Ethics Institute, Christchurch, New Zealand.

Maddox J (1991) 'The case for the human genome', *Nature*, 352 (11).

Marteau TM & Croyle RT (1998) 'Psychological responses to genetic testing', *BMJ*, 316, pp.693-696.

Marteau T & Richards M (1996) *The Troubled Helix. Social and pyschological implications of the new human genetics*, Cambridge University Press.

McLean S (1994) 'Mapping the Human Genome – friend or foe', *Soc. Sci. Med*, 39, pp.1221-1227.

McLean S (1997) speaking on 'Analysis', BBC Radio 4, 16 February.

Mintel Marketing Intelligence (1996) *Genetic Testing: Insurance implications and Consumer Views*, Mintel International Group Limited, London.

Murray J Cuckle H (1997) 'Screening for fragile X syndrome', *Journal of Medical Screening*, 4, pp.60-94.

National Screening Committee (1998) *First Report of the National Screening Committee*, Department of Health, HMSO, London.

Nature (1996) Editorial: 'Keep an eye on genetic screening', 384, p.93 14 November.

Nature (1997a), 'No consensus on FDA role in gene tests', Meredith Wadman, 386, p.531, 10 April.

Nature (1997b), 'Are patents and research compatible?', Philippe Ducor, 387, 1 May.

Nature (1997c), 'US urged to monitor some genetic tests', Meredith Wadman, 385, p.477, 6 February.

NHS Executive (1998) Health Service Circular 'The New NHS – modern and dependable', HSC 1998/139

Nuffield Council on Bioethics (1993) *Genetic screening: ethical issues*, London.

Orton P & Fry J (1995) *UK Health Care: The Facts*, Kulwer.

Pokorski RJ (1998) 'A test for the insurance industry', *Nature*, 391, pp.835-836.

Post SG et al (1997) *Journal of American Medical Association*, 277, pp.832-836.

Royal College of Physicians (1989) *Prenatal Diagnosis and Genetic Screening: Community and service implications*, London.

Royal College of Physicians (1991) *Purchasers' guidelines to genetics servces in the NHS*, London.

Royal College of Physicians (1996) *Clinical Genetic Services into the 21st Century*, London.

Royal College of Physicians (1998) *Clinical Genetic Services. Activity, outcome, effectiveness and quality*, London.

Royal Society of Medicine conference (1995) *Genetics in Primary Care*, 18 November.

Silver L (1998) *Remaking Eden: Cloning and beyond in a brave new world*, Weidenfeld and Nicholson, London.

Skyes R (1997) *The New genetics: A universal panacea or pandora's box?*, Royal College of Physicians Lumleian Lecture, 15 May, GlaxoWellcome.

The Guardian (1997a) 'It's official: we've all got sex on the brain', Jerome Burner, 27 May, p.13.

The Guardian (1997b) 'Rock-a-bye baby with the perfect genes', George Monbiot, 18 February.

The Observer (1997a) 'The pill: women are denied new life or death safety test', Peter Beaumont, 25 May, p.1.

The Observer (1997b) 'The Watchdogs didn't bite. In fact, they barely even barked', Business Section, 25 May, p.7.

Tversky, Amos and Kahneman D (1986) 'Rational choice and the framing of decisions', *Journal of Business* Vol 59, No 4, pp.251-278

TUC Equal Rights Department (1997) *Genetic Testing by Employers*, May.

Vidal J (1998) 'Desperately seeking Viagra', *The Guardian*, 26 September, p.3.

Welsh Health Planning Forum (1995) *Genomics: The Impact of Genetics on the New NHS*, Cardiff

Welsh Institute for Health and Social Care (1998) *Report of the Citizens' Jury on Genetic testing for Common Disorders*, University of Glamorgan.

Wilke T (1997) 'The Regulation of Human Genetics in Britain' in Towse A and Laughton-Smith H (ed) *Regulation in the Pharmaceutical Industry* Macmillan (forthcoming).

Williams S & Calnan (1996) 'The limits of medicalisation? Modern medicine and lay populace in "late" modernity', *Soc. Sci. Med*, 42(12), pp.1609-1620.

Wilson JMG & Junger G (1968) *Principle and Practice of Screening for Disease*, World Health Organisation, Geneva.

World Health Organisation (1985) *The Heriditatry Diseases programme*, Document No. HMG/WG/85.10, Geneva, Switzerland.

World Health Organisation (1991) *Community genetics services in Europe*, regional publication, European Series No.38.

Zimmern R (1998a) *Report of consensus meeting on the mangement of women with a family history of breast cancer*, Unit for Public Health Genetics, Cambridge & Huntingdon Health Authority.

Zimmern R (1998b) *Genetic Testing, a Conceptual Exploration*, Unit for Public Health Genetics, Cambridge & Huntingdon Health Authority.